M·J·Montgolfier afcending
with 6 other Persons from
Lyons in France 1784.

The Dream Machines

Vincent Lunardi ascending in
his Grand British Colour'd Balloon
from the Artillery Ground, London
1785.

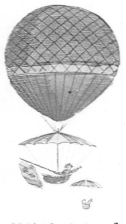

M·Blanchards Ascenfion from
Lisle Augt 1785 & the Experiment
of the Parachute and Dog.

M. Garnerin and Captⁿ Sowden's
Ascent from Ranelagh Gardens
June 28th 1802.

Filling a Balloon

Peter Haining

Descending in a
Parachute.

"What was the general astonishment when the inventors of the machine announced that immediately it should be full of gas, which they had the means of producing at will by the most simple process, it would raise itself to the clouds! It must be granted that, in spite of the confidence in the ingenuity and experience of the Montgolfiers, this fear seemed too incredible, so like unto a dream, to these who came to witness it, that the persons who knew most about it—who were, at the same time, the most favourably predisposed in its favour—doubted of its success."
FAUJAS de SAINT FOND
La Description Des
Experiences De La Machine
Aerostatique (1783)

"Whether aerostation becomes a professional art, or is given up with the prosecution of the Tower of Babel and other invasions on the coast of Heaven, such writings as are made by observers or the argonauts themselves will always be a precious curiosity."
HORACE WALPOLE
Letter to Lady Ossary
July, 1785

The Dream Machines

Peter Haining

WORLD PUBLISHING
TIMES MIRROR

Contents

Copyright ©
Peter Haining 1971, 1972
Foreword, linking text and
translations copyright ©
Peter Haining 1971
Introduction copyright ©
Lord Montague of Beaulieu 1972
First published in United States
1973 by World Publishing
Printed and bound in Great Britain

ISBN 0 529 04705 5

Chronology of Ballooning

1783 First hot-air balloon demonstrated by Montgolfier Brothers at Annonay. June 5th.

1783 First manned voyage in hot-air balloon by Marquis D'Arlandes and Pilatre de Rozier. Paris, November 21st.

1783 First voyage in a hydrogen balloon, by Charles and Robert at Paris, December 1st.

1784 The first woman to fly, Madame Thible, ascends as a passenger at Lyons. June 4th.

1784 First aerial voyage in England by Vincent Lunardi. September 15th.

1784 First English-born aeronaut, Sadler, makes his ascent. October 4th.

1785 First Channel crossing, by Blanchard and Jeffries. January 7th.

1785 The first balloon fatality (de Rozier and Romain) near Boulogne. June 15th.

1785 Mrs. Sage, the first Englishwoman aeronaut, ascends from London. June 29th.

1793 First aerial voyage in U.S.A. by Blanchard. January 9th.

1794 Balloons first used for military observation, by the French at Mauberge. June 2nd.

1797 First parachute descent, by Garnerin, at Paris. October 22nd.

1821 Green's first ascent and the introduction of coal gas. July 19th.

1836 The "Vauxhall Balloon" flight from London to Weilburg (Nassau)—480 miles in 18 hours. November 7th-8th.

1844 Coxwell's first ascent. August 19th.

1849 First bombing raid by balloons. The bombs attached to un-manned hot-air balloons, sent over Venice by the Austrians.

1859 American balloonist John Wise makes record flight from St. Louis to Henderson, N.Y. (809 miles in 19 hours 50 minutes.) July 2nd.

1861-3 Balloons used for observation in the American Civil War.

1870-1 Over 60 balloons escape from besieged Paris.

1873 First attempt to cross the Atlantic from New York fails. October 6th.

1892 Experiments begin with small pilot balloons to carry meteorological instruments. Still in use.

1897 Andree leaves Danes Island on his fatal North Pole flight. July 11th.

1906 First Gordon Bennett balloon race. Paris, September 30th.

1913 Duration record of 87 hours set up by Kaulen. December.

1914 Distance record of 1,890 miles set up by Berliner from Bitterfield to Kirgischan in the Urals. February.

1914-18 Kite balloons used for observation by German and Allied forces.

1931 Professor Piccard makes first stratosphere flight from Augsburg and reaches height of 9½ miles.

1961 Two American Navy officers set world's altitude record for gas balloon of 113,740 ft.

1966 World record for hot air balloon established at 28,582 ft. in America.

Foreword

Peter Haining

"It was exactly like going to Heaven in a washing tub or an omnibus—and in those regions, separated from all human associations, the soul might almost fancy it had passed the confines of the grave."
'IN NUBIBUS,' Weekly Chronicle 1820

"It's a dream. My dream, but anyone else can have a piece. It's a giant, floating, magic mushroom that grows on air and heat instead of cold and damp."
LINK BAUM, American Balloonist 1971

Two views on the delights of ballooning, written some 150 years apart yet identical in their author's obvious relish of new sensations and excitement. Indeed, contained in them is just a little of the essence which makes this activity perhaps the most unique personal experience open to man. A silent, soaring, magic carpet ride to the skies in your own dream machine.

Man has sought to raise himself out of his natural element since the very earliest times, and despite the numerous and usually fatal leaps of winged men and tower jumpers, it was not until 1783, and thanks to the pioneer efforts of the Montgolfier Brothers (their name, incidentally, means "Master of the Mountain") that he finally achieved this object in a hot air balloon. Since then balloons have been superseded in turn by the aeroplane and, of late, by the space rocket, yet somehow, magically and marvellously, they have retained their faithful aeronauts and constant admirers. Progress may indeed have passed them by—yet their appeal is timeless and their attraction in our society of noise and bustle and strife a fact to be welcomed and applauded.

This book, then, is a salute to these leviathans of the air—a celebration in the words of those who have experienced their pleasures and their dangers. Linked to the reports are contemporary pictures and drawings which illustrate nearly two hundred years of ballooning. The collection is, of course, far from comprehensive and it attempts to do no more than outline the history of balloons—both hot air and hydrogen—from their inception in France, through to the development of the airship and the pioneer work of Alberto Santos-Dumont. There are also a few illustrations to underline the continuing interest in balloons, but as much of the aeronautical literature of the past fifty years is readily available, no attempt has been made to duplicate it.

In compiling the collection I have laid considerable emphasis on two points: firstly, that each contributor had actual ballooning experience and, secondly, that all were famous—men and women whose names are familiar far beyond the confines of aeronautics. My aim here has been not only to satisfy the enthusiast who may well not be aware of the attraction balloons have had for certain famous authors, but also the general reader seeking an introduction to ballooning through those similarly attracted by its magic but not bound by its technicalities. My reading has taken me from the exceedingly rare treatise "The Air Balloon" (which reported sceptically in 1783 that "the public will readily see that little or no use can be made of it") through the reports of the first balloonists Montgolfier, D'Arlandes and Charles (not forgetting the Mesdames Blanchard, Sage and Graham) to the stories of Jules Verne and Edgar Allan Poe (his tale "The Balloon Hoax" was almost literally responsible for stimulating the American public's interest in ballooning) to the famous balloon expeditions of Andree ("the most heroic exploit in the annals of flight") and finally today's increasingly successful balloon rallies in Britain, Europe and America. It is a literature of great adventures, heart-stopping drama, intrigue, death and not a little humour.

In making my final selection I have endeavoured to avoid over-familiar items and purposely not covered the more recent events such as the Gordon Bennett Races, the various altitude and long distance record attempts and the flights of men such as Fred Dolder, Don Cameron, Don Piccard and Anthony Smith (his account of a 'Balloon Safari' across Africa told in "Throw Out Two Hands" is required reading for any enthusiast) because, simply, they are easily obtainable. I have tried, too, to have each item relate to the next in such a way that the book presents—albeit briefly—a history in fact and fiction of ballooning.

Today, I need hardly add, the interest in balloons is such that they create enormous interest wherever they appear and draw crowds which rival those who witnessed the ascents of the early pioneers. They have also become the subject matter for films (see our special appendix), popular songs (who has not hummed "Up, Up and Away"?), art (Graham Steven's 'inflatables') and an increasing number of books. Truly, the appeal of Man's first aerial vehicle—his Dream Machine—is ageless and its attraction enduring.

Welcome, then, to the world of the Lords of the Silent Skies.

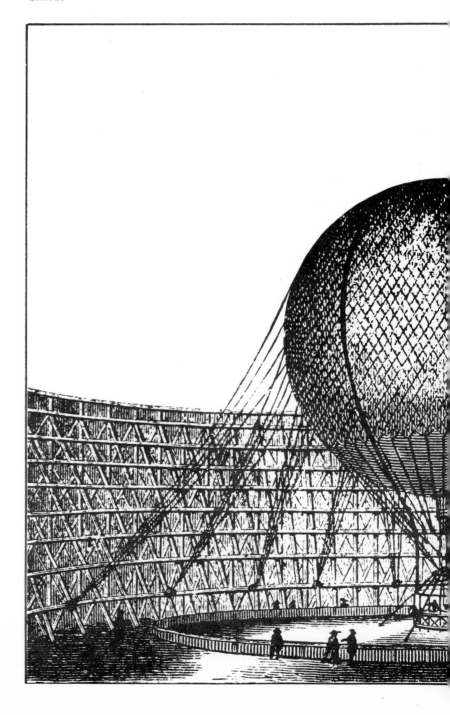

Introduction

Lord Montague of Beaulieu

Mention any mode of transport — be it the bicycle or the aeroplane — and you launch immediately into a saga of progress, from romantic and unpractical exploration to universal acceptance. In 1908 a flight of ten miles was a major achievement: in 1928 you made the headlines if you flew from London to Sydney: but forty years later a businessman with adequate funds and a tight schedule would never contemplate any other means of travel between the two cities. The ancestors of to-day's Fords, Fiats, Renaults and Opels found it hard to cope with a twenty-mile non-stop trip; now they crowd the world's highways, though the spirit of adventure has been lost in the process of evolution. There is, however, one mode of travel that has never grown up, and that is the balloon.

Free balloons have travelled long distances: they have ascended to the stratosphere; they have stayed aloft for days on end; but their practical value has always been restricted. There may be a parallel between Montgolfier's eighteenth-century exploits with livestock and the space-dog Laika: but in a decade men have reached the moon. In close on two hundred years the balloon is still the epitome of travelling hopefully.

These 'dream machines' were innocent of any spirit of urgency. *Bon viveurs* of the stamp of Frank Hedges Butler could dine off cold chicken and champagne while watching the lights of London from three thousand feet up — admittedly this can be done with the aid of a modern helicopter, but the method lacks repose. Unlike primitive aeroplanes, (and motor-cars, for that matter) the balloon did not demand layers of ursine apparel — hence Butler's daughter Vera could assure ladies that aeronatics was a sport in which they could share 'without loss of dignity or mannishness'. For the fanciful there were new and exciting vistas — clouds were transformed into glaciers and cemeteries into gigantic sets of dominoes.

Alongside this romantic indolence there were, of course, the miseries. A balloon could descend where it wished, but its ascent was dependent on a supply of gas, and this meant a municipal gasworks. Hurlingham owed its status as the aeronaut's Ascot to its proximity to the gasholders of Fulham. Wind and weather could blow one to Brussels; it could also keep one drifting over the Essex marshes while the captain navigated as best he could from a copy of Bradshaw's Railway Guide.

But for all the olfactory diversions and physical perils of the gasworks, here was the perfect gentleman's sport. One was dependent on one's tender care, expecially on occasions when winds blew the balloon across the Thames eight times. Only the leisured classes were proof against the embarassment of descending into the middle of a garden party, of a trail-rope unleashed on a huddle of greenhouses. If one landed on the vicarage lawn, it was tea for the aeronauts: if in a gipsy encampment, they got gin. A sense of humour was desirable, for anything could be impressed as ballast in emergencies, and Charles Stewart Rolls objected to careless passengers who flung their chicken-bones overboard as they ate. The ballon's very lack of control could lead it into infelicitous landing places, as a French aeronaut discovered when his craft settled in the hop-fields around Alton. 'I never knew', he observed bitterly, 'that the English grew their blasted beer on trees'.

Motorists took to the balloon as a protest against noise, vibration and an over-zealous constabulary. Soon, however, they discovered that there was precious little one could do with a balloon. An international race might start from Paris, but the wise aeronaut armed himself with visas valid for Austria and even Russia — just in case; while his phrase-book embraced Russian, Italian, and, as a last resort, Latin. A favourite — and viable — sport was Hare and Hounds, in which the hare wore distinctive streamers and was forbidden to make intermediate landings. The prize, however, went to the hound who landed nearest to the hare, and a distance of four miles was considered good going, even though Charles Rolls once nearly got himself caught by an involvement with some telephone wires.

The Dream Machines is indeed an apposite title for such an evocative work, even though a pedant would doubtless object on the grounds that there was no machinery — merely gas to valve, and ballast to throw out. Their very aimlessness was recognised even by landlubbers, as witness the apocryphal tale of the yokel who, when asked by a puzzled aeronaut where he was, responded calmly: 'Why, up in a balloon'. Let us hope that some day the sport may be seriously revived: after all, it is not impossibly expensive, and there is a lot of sky left over from to-day's complicated airways network.

The New Sensation of Balloons

Benjamin Franklin

One of the earliest reports of Ballooning was this letter by Benjamin Franklin, (1706-1790) later to become perhaps America's greatest statesmen. Addressed to a medical friend in Vienna, it conveys not only the writer's enthusiasm for 'the new sensation' but also his very real understanding of the art. At the time of writing, Franklin was a diplomat in Paris.

Monsieur le Dr. Ingenhauss,
Medecin de sa Majeste Imperiale,
Vienna.

Passy, Jan. 16th, 1784

Dear Friend,

I now sit down to give you every Information in my Power respecting the new Sensation of Balloons. There is no Secret in the Affair, and I make no doubt that a Person could easily obtain a sight of the Balloons with all the Instructions wanted; and if you undertake to make one, I think it extremely proper and necessary to send an ingenious Man here for that purpose: otherwise for want of attention to some particular circumstance, or of being acquainted with it, the Experiment might miscarry, which being in an Affair of so much public expectation, would have bad Consequences, draw upon you a great deal of Censure, and affect your Reputation. It is a serious thing to draw out from their Affairs all the inhabitants of a great City and its Environs, and a Disappointment makes them angry. At Bordeaux lately a Person who pretended to send up a Balloon & had received Money of many People, not being able to make it rise, the Populace were so exasperated they pull'd down his House, and had like to have kill'd him.

It appears to be a Discovery of great Importance, and one which may possibly give a new Turn to human Affairs. Convincing sovereigns of the Folly of Wars, may perhaps be one Effect of it: since it will be impractible for the most potent of them to guard his Dominions. Five Thousand Balloons capable of raising two Men each, would not cost more than Five ships of the line: And where is the Prince who can afford so to cover his Country with troops for its Defence, as that Ten Thousand Men descending from the Clouds, might not in many Places do an infinite deal of Mischief, before a Force could be brought together to repel them?

It is a pity that any national Jealousy should prevent the English from prosecuting the Experiment, since they are such Ingenious Mechanicians, that in their Hands it might have made a more rapid Progress towards Perfect & all the Utility it is capable of affording.

One of the balloons I have seen was fill'd with inflammable Air. The quantity being great as it is expensive & tedious in filling, requiring two or more Days & Nights constant Labour. It had a Soupape near the Top, which the aeronauts could open by pulling a String, and therefore let out some Air when they had a mind to descend; and they discharged some of their Ballast of Sand, when they would rise again. A great deal of Air must have been let out when they landed, so that the loose Part might envelope one of them; yet the Car being lighted by that one getting out of it, there is enough left to carry up the other rapidly. They had no Fire with them. That is us'd only in the hot air Globe; which is open at the Bottom, and Straw constantly burnt to keep it up. This kind is sooner cheaper fill'd; but must be much bigger to carry up the same Weight; since Air rarify'd by Heat is only twice as light as common Air, & inflammable Air ten times lighter.

We shall Doubtless hear more of these Balloons and the Men who Experiment with them and I ask you, my Dear Friend, to Study all that you can on the matter. Nor can I now add further but that I am, as ever,

Yours most affectionately,

Benj. Franklin

The First Ascent

Etienne Montgolfier

No name is more famous in the annals of Ballooning than Montgolfier and here the younger of the two Brothers, Étienne Montgolfier (1745-1799), who pioneered the art of hot air balloons graphically describes the day when aeronautics at last became a reality.

The aerostatic machine launched at Annonay, 5 June 1783 was constructed of cloth lined with paper, fastened together on a network of strings fixed to the cloth. It was spherical; its circumference was 110 feet, and a wooden frame sixteen feet square held it fixed at the bottom. Its contents were about 22,000 cubic feet, and it accordingly displaced a volume of air weighing 1,980 lbs.

The weight of the gas was nearly half the weight of the air, for it weighed 990 lbs., and the machine itself, with the frame, weighed 500 lbs: it was, therefore, impelled upwards with the force of 490 lbs.

Two men sufficed to raise it and to fill it with gas, but it took eight to hold it down till the signal was given. The different pieces of the covering were fastened together with buttons and button-holes.

It remained ten minutes in the air, but the loss of gas by the button-holes, and by other imperfections, did not permit it to continue longer. The wind at the moment of the ascent was from the north.

The machine finally came down so lightly that no part of it was broken.

The birth of ballooning at Annonay in France on June 5, 1783. In the contemporary illustration opposite, the Montgolfier Brothers demonstrate their hot air 'envelope' to the public. Acknowledgement of the achievement took many forms including a statue of the Brothers erected by the King, Louis XVI, and their appearance in a multitude of lauditory illustrations published throughout Europe (below).

A puffing up the Air Balloon.

You now behold it fill'd quite soon.

Now tis gone quite out of sight.

Behold the Moon that shines so bright.

Now the Balloon appears again

Here you may veiw it very plain

The people stare to see it fly

Zooks it has got surprizing high.

A man in the Moon but not asleep.

Old Cacofagus takes a peep.

The clowns are frighten'd at the sight

'Tis burst and now is come down quite.

English magazines and journals in the main tended to treat ballooning rather less than seriously. National pride that the French had invented the balloon probably accounts for a good deal of this scepticism, but the British authorities were convinced that it had really very little practical use and if there was a future this would be limited to entertaining the populace — as this group of pictures published as a broadsheet in May 1784 indicates. The strip, one of a series published by John Hawkins of Temple Bar, London, proved enormously popular and sold in excess of 100,000 copies at ½p each.

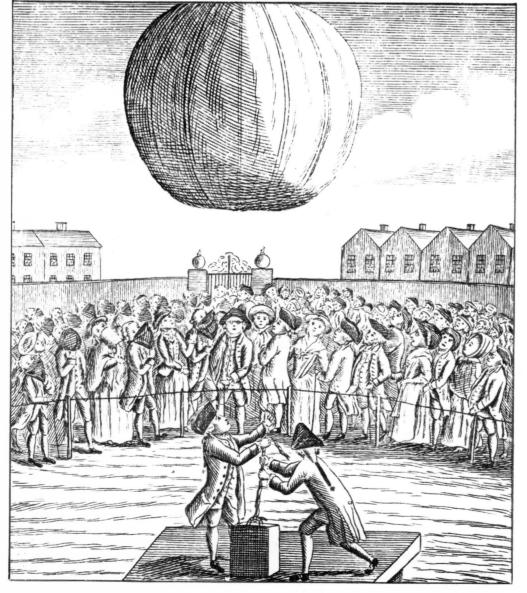

The early public demonstrations of balloons attracted large and curious crowds in both France and England. The first picture (opposite) depicts the fourth experiment by Montgolfier on September 19 1783 which drew a huge assembly to the square at Versailles. The event was witnessed by the King, Louis XVI, and was the first voyage with 'living' passengers — a basket was suspended beneath the balloon containing a sheep and some pigeons. (Above) A French professor explains the 'Nature of a Balloon' from a print of 1784. In the third illustration the launching of the first English experimental balloon at the Artillery Ground, London on November 25 1783 is shown. Note how many members of the audience are peering nervously from behind their hats at this 'marvellous occurrence'!

The First Manned Voyage

Marquis D'Arlandes

MARQUIS D'ARLANDES

PILATRE DE ROZIER

The great moment in history when man at last lifted himself off the ground and into a new element was actually shared by two French pioneers the Marquis D'Arlandes (1742-1802) and his colleague Pilâtre de Rozier (1756-1785). D'Arlandes a brave and courageous nobleman here records the journey which turned a million dreams into reality.

I wish to describe as well as I can the first journey which men have attempted through an element which, prior to the discovery of MM. Montgolfier, seemed so little fitted to support them.

We went up on the 21st of October, 1783, at near two o'clock, M. Rozier on the west side of the balloon, I on the east. The wind was nearly north-west. The machine, say the public, rose with majesty; but really the position of the balloon altered so that M. Rozier was in the advance of our position, I in the rear.

I was surprised at the silence and the absence of movement which our departure caused among the spectators, and believed them to be astonished and perhaps awed at the strange spectacle; they might well have reassured themselves. I was still gazing, when M. Rozier cried to me—

'You are doing nothing, and the balloon is scarcely rising a fathom.'

'Pardon me', I answered, as I placed a bundle of straw upon the fire and slightly stirred it. Then I turned quickly, but already we had passed out of sight of La Muette. Astonished I cast a glance towards the river. I perceived the confluence of the Oise. And naming the principal bends of the river by the places nearest them, I cried, 'Passy, St. Germain, St. Denis, Sèvres!'

'If you look at the river in that fashion you will be likely to bathe in it soon,' cried Rozier. 'Some fire, my dear friend, some fire!'

We travelled on; but instead of crossing the river, as our direction seemed to indicate, we bore towards the Invalides, then returned upon the principal bend of the river, and travelled to above the barrier of La Conference, thus dodging about the river, but not crossing it.

'The river is very difficult to cross,' I remarked to my companion.

'So it seems,' he answered; 'but you are doing nothing. I suppose it is because you are braver than I, and don't fear a tumble.'

I stirred the fire; I seized a truss of straw with my fork; I raised it and threw it in the midst of the flames. An instant afterwards I felt myself lifted as if it were into the heavens.

'For once we move,' said I.

'Yes, we move,' answered my companion.

At the same instant I heard from the top of the balloon a sound which made me believe that it had burst. I watched, yet I saw nothing. My companion had gone into the interior, no doubt to make some observations. As my eyes were fixed on the top of the machine I experienced a shock, and it was the only one I had yet felt. The direction of the movement was from above, downwards. I then said—

'What are you doing Are you having a dance to yourself'

'I'm not moving.'

'So much the better. It is only a new current which I hope will carry us from the river,' I answered.

I turned to see where we were, and found we were between the Ecole Militaire and the Invalides.

'We are getting on,' said Rozier.

'Yes, we are travelling.'

The first manned balloon flight crosses Paris on November 21, 1783.
The pioneer aeronauts were Pilatre de Rozier and his friend the
Marquid D'Arlandes who had to obtain special permission for the
flight from Louis XVI, as His Majesty had decreed that the first men
to go up in the new invention should be two convicted criminals. In
fact the moment when man finally took the skies went off without
any undue problem and the twenty-five minute flight took the
aeronauts just five and a half miles.

Three of the many souvenir illustrations and miniatures which were produced to commemorate the flight of Rozier and D'Arlandes. The picture containing the oval portrait of one Giroud de Villette (below, left) is interesting in that this man claimed it was he who should have made the first voyage with Rozier. Their journey was planned for October 19 1783, but when the balloon proved unsuitable the attempt was abandoned, and in the subsequent flight Villette was replaced by the Marquis D'Arlandes.

(Opposite). One of the earliest German ascents—Herr Adorne rising above Strasbourg in March 1784. Unfortunately the balloon crashed on the rooftops after only being airborn for a few minutes.

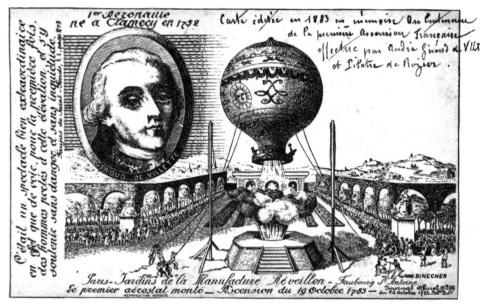

'Let us work, let us work,' said he.

I now heard another report in the machine, which I believed was produced by the cracking of a cord. This new intimation made me carefully examine the inside of our habitation. I saw that the part that was turned towards the south was full of holes, of which some were of a considerable size.

'It must descend,' I then cried.

'Why'

'Look!' I said. At the same time I took my sponge and quietly extinguished the fire that was burning some of holes within my reach; but at the same moment I perceived that the bottom of the cloth was coming away from the circle which surrounded it.

'We must descend,' I repeated to my companion.

He looked below.

'We are upon Paris,' he said.

'It does not matter,' I answered. 'Only look! Is there no danger? Are you holding on well'

'Yes.'

I examined from my side, and saw that we had nothing to fear. I then tried with my sponge the ropes which were within my reach. All of them held firm. Only two of the cords had broken.

I then said, 'We can cross Paris.'

During this operation we were rapidly getting down to the roofs. We made more fire, and rose again with the greatest ease. I looked down, and it seemed to me we were going towards the towers of St. Sulpice; but, on rising, a new current made us quit this direction and bear more to the south. I looked to the left, and beheld a wood, which I believed to be that of Luxembourg. We were traversing the boulevard, and I cried all at once—

'Get to ground!'

But the intrepid Rozier, who never lost his head, and who judged more surely than I, prevented me from attempting to descend. I then threw a bundle of straw on the fire. We rose again, and another current bore us to the left. We were now close to the ground, between two mills. As soon as we came near the earth I raised myself over the gallery, and leaning there with my two hands, I felt the balloon pressing softly against my head. I pushed it back, and leaped down to the ground. Looking round and expecting to see the balloon still distended, I was astonished to find it quite empty and flattened. On looking for Rozier I saw him in his shirt-sleeves creeping from under the mass of canvas that had fallen over him. Before attempting to descend he had put off his coat and placed it in the basket. After a deal of trouble we were at last all right.

As Rozier was without a coat I besought him to go to the nearest house. On his way thither he encountered the Duke of Chartres, who had followed us, as we saw, very closely, for I had had the honour of conversing with him the moment before we set out.

The Mechanic Meteors

Horace Walpole

The interest and support for the new science was by no means universal and sceptics abounded in the highest spheres of business and public life. Here the great English essayist and novelist, Horace Walpole (1717-1797) expresses the views of all those who felt the experiments of aerostation were no more than a wild fantasy doomed to failure.

Do not wonder that today we do not entirely attend to things of earth: Fashion has ascended to a higher element. All our views are directed to the air. Balloons occupy senators, philosophers, ladies, everybody. France gave us the *ton;* and, as yet, we have not come up to our model. Their monarch is so struck with the heroism of two of his subjects (the brothers Joseph and Etienne Montgolfier) who adventured their persons in two of these new floating batteries, that he has ordered statues of them, and contributed a vast sum towards their marble immortality.

All this may be very important; to me it looks somewhat foolish. Very early in my life I remember this town (Twickenham) at gaze on a man who flew down a rope from the top of St. Martin's steeple; now, late in my day, people are staring at a voyage to the moon. The former Icarus broke his neck at a subsequent flight: when a similar accident happens to modern knight-errants, adieu to air-balloons.

In truth, I hope these new mechanic meteors will prove only playthings for the learned and the idle, and not be converted into new engines of destruction to the human race, as is often the case of refinements or discoveries in science. The wicked wit of man always studies to apply the results of talents to enslaving, destroying, or cheating his fellow creatures. Could we reach the moon, we should think of reducing it to a province of some European Kingdom.

If, however, these balloons can be improved into anything more than Brobdignag kites, it must be in a century or two after I shall be laid low. A century in my acceptation means a hundred years hence, or a year or two hence, for after one ceases to be, all duration is of the same length; and everything that one guesses will happen after one's self is no more, is equally a vision. Visions I loved, while they decked with rainbows, or concealed the clouds of the horizon before me; but now that the dream is so near to an end, I have no occasion for lesser pageants—much less for divining with what airy vehicles the atmosphere will be peopled hereafter, or how much more

expeditiously the East, West, or South, will be ravaged and butchered, than they have been by the old-fashioned, clumsy method of navigation.

It is true, I do not shut my eyes to the follies actually before them. I smile at the adoration paid to these aerial Quixotes; and reflect, that as formerly men were admired for their lives in order to destroy others; now they are worshipped for venturing their necks *en pure perte*—much more commendably I do allow; yet fame is the equal object of both. I smile, too, at the stupidity that pays a guinea for being allowed to see what any man may see by holding up his head and looking at the sky: and I observe that no improvements of science or knowledge make the world a jot wiser; knowledge, like reason, being a fine tool that will give an exquisite polish or finishing to ornaments; but is not strong enough to answer the common occasions of mankind.

I learn from the accounts of the airgonauts themselves that they were exactly like birds; they flew through the air, perched on the top of a tree—the smugglers, I suppose, will be the first that will improve on the plan. However, if the project is ever brought

to any perfection (though I apprehend it will be addled like the ship that was to live under the water and never came up again*) it will have a different fate from other discoveries whose inventors are not known. In this age all that is done (as well as what is never done) is so faithfully recorded, that every improvement will be registered chronologically. It all puts me in mind of Dryden's "Indian Emperor":

What divine monsters, O ye gods, are these,
That float in air, and fly upon the seas!

Dryden little thought that he was prophetically describing something more exactly than ships as conceived by Mexicans. If there is no air-sickness it may also be found that people will prefer the balloon to the packet-boat should they wish to cross the Channel!
(1783-1785)

(*This early 'submarine' was the handiwork of a man named Day who sank it in 17 fathoms of water at Plymouth in June 1774. When he failed to surface after 12 hours as he had claimed, a search was made, but neither the craft nor its occupant were ever recovered. *Editor's Note*).

After the achievements of the first balloonists, speculation about their potential was rife in Europe. The essayists and satirists of the time gave the aeronauts and their 'machines' particular attention as the illustrations here show. In the picture opposite the general populace are marvelling at the somewhat fanciful balloons of Montgolfier and Katterfelto — both of whom appear to be in imminent danger of attack from the Devil for invading his realm! In the smaller picture (above) Montgolfier's invention is proposed in humourous vein in a newspaper as the 'French Aerial Navy' of the future.

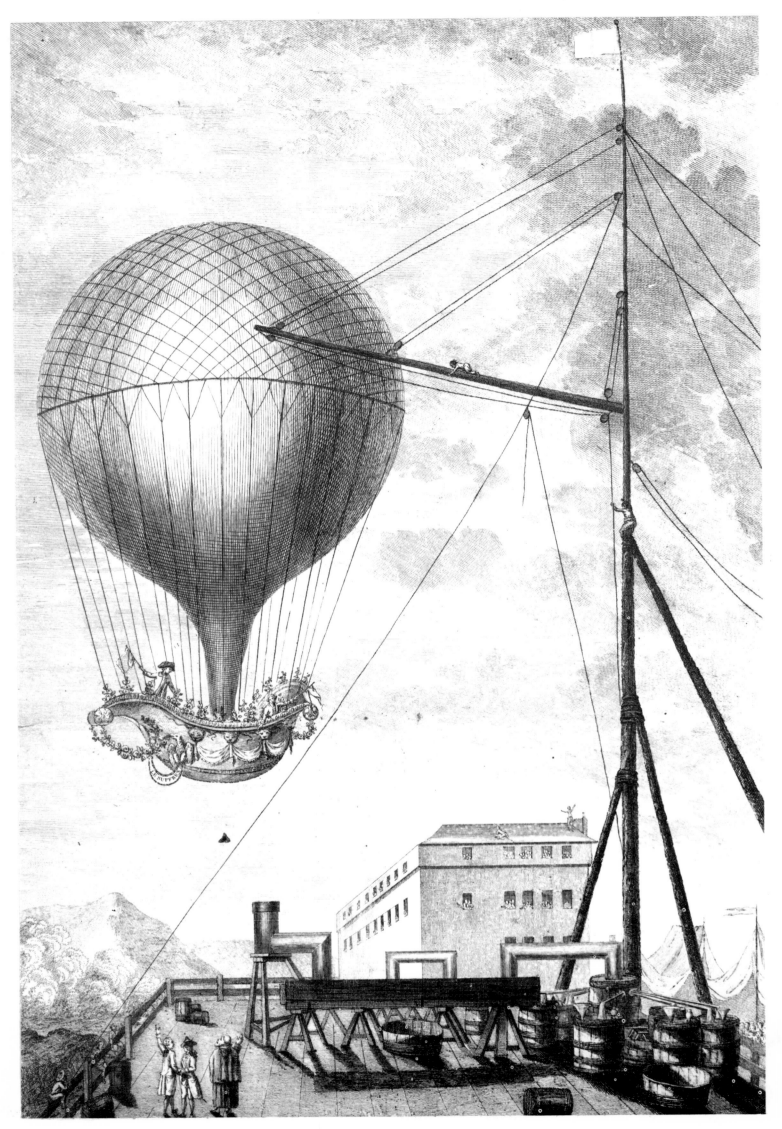

With all the success which surrounded the early balloonists it was easy to forget the very real dangers which these men faced whenever they ascended to the heavens. And, sadly, it was not to be long before the first pioneer met his death — Pilatre de Rozier, in 1785. The pioneer aeronaut was seeking to advance the art of ballooning and designed a new aerostat with a hydrogen envelope at the top and a hot-air cylinder beneath. To test it he ascended with his companion M. Romain from Calais on the morning of June 15th, intending to cross the Channel to England. He had barely reached the coast, however, when the hydrogen was set alight and the balloon crashed, near Boulogne, killing both men instantly. In the first print (above, left), the two balloonists and their experimental craft rise majestically above the ships in Calais. In the second, the moment of disaster is recorded in a plate drawn some years later.

Undeterred by this sad incident the balloonists continued to persevere with their experiments while several set their sights not on the channel but on crossing mountain ranges. In the third illustration (opposite) a balloon designed especially to traverse the Alps is shown undergoing tests at its base close to the foothills. The balloon, "Le Suffren" is piloted by Coustard de Massi and R. P. Mouchet.

The Second Aerial Expedition

Professor Charles

France continued to lead the way in aerial experiment as this account of the second manned balloon flight shows. Professor Jacques Charles (1746-1822) was accompanied for part of his flight by one of the famed French engineering brothers, M. Robert, but after a preliminary landing carried on for some distance on his own—thus becoming the first solo balloonist. It is perhaps surprising to note that after the spectacular success of the voyage, Professor Charles never again went up in a balloon. However, his daring set the example for all those who were to follow.

The day set for the ascent of Mr. Robert and myself was the 1st of December 1783. A multitude of Parisians had assembled at our launching site in the Tuileries when we arrived and there was great excitement about this second expedition by man into the skies.

A little after mid-day when all our arrangements were complete, I asked for the cannon to be sounded to announce our departure. I then stepped across to M. Montgolier who had come to watch our ascent and presented to him a miniature balloon with the words, "It is for you, monsieur, to show us the way to the skies."

The balloon which escaped from the hands of M. Montgolfier, rose into the air, and seemed to carry with it the testimony of friendship and regard between that gentleman and myself, while acclamations followed it.

Meanwhile, we hastily prepared for departure. The stormy weather did not permit us to have at our command all the arrangements which we had contemplated the previous evening; to do so would have detained us too long upon the earth. After the balloon and the car were in equilibrium, we threw over 19 lbs. of ballast, and we rose in the midst of silence, arising from the emotion and surprise felt on all sides.

Nothing will ever equal that moment of joyous excitement which filled my whole being when I felt myself flying away from the earth. It was not mere pleasure; it was perfect bliss. Escaped from the frightful torments of persecution and of calumny, I felt that I was answering all in rising above all.

To this sentiment succeeded one more lively still—the admiration of the majestic spectacle that spread itself out before us. On whatever side we looked, all was glorious; a cloudless sky above, a most delicious view around. 'Oh, my friend,' said I to M. Robert, 'how great is our good fortune! I care not what may be the condition of the earth; it is the sky that is for me now. What serenity! what a ravishing scene! Would that I could bring here the last of our detractors, and say to the wretch, Behold what you would have lost had you arrested the progress of science.'

With some justification it has been claimed that Professor Charles, the scientist and official instructor at the Louvre in Paris, created the art of aerostation. He introduced hydrogen as the means of inflating the balloon and also the various inventions which made it complete: a valve for control of the air, the car or basket to carry passengers, the sand for ballast, the coating of caoutchouc which made the balloon air-tight and the barometer to measure the elevation. In the first picture here (above right) Professor Charles is seen conducting his initial experiments with his assistants the Parisian engineering brothers, Collin and Hullin Robert. In the next (above, top) they take the balloon by night to its launching point in the Champ de Mars. Finally (above) the passengerless balloon was released on the afternoon of August 27 1783 and the balloon soared away to come to rest eventually in the small village of Gonesse. The local peasants were so terrified by the arrival of this strange object from the skies that, believing it to be some kind of animal, they literally hacked it to pieces with their scythes and forks!

Whilst we were rising with a progressively increasing speed, we waved our bannerets in token of our cheerfulness, and in order to give confidence to those below who took an interest in our fate. M. Robert made an inventory of our stores; our friends had stocked our commissariat as for a long voyage—champagne and other wines, garments of fur and other articles of clothing.

'Good,' I said; 'throw that out of the window.' He took a blanket and launched it into the air, through which it floated down slowly, and fell upon the dome of l'Assomption.

When the barometer had fallen 26 inches, we ceased to ascend. We were up at an elevation of 1,800 feet. This was the height to which I had promised myself to ascend; and, in fact, from this moment to the time when we disappeared from the eyes of our friends, we always kept a horizontal course, the barometer registering 26 inches to 26 inches 8 lines.

We required to throw over ballast in proportion as the almost insensible escape of the hydrogen gas caused us to descend, in order to remain as nearly as possible at the same elevation. If circumstances had permitted us to measure the amount of ballast we threw over, our course would have been almost absolutely horizontal.

After remaining for a few moments stationary, our car changed its course, and we were carried on at the will of the wind. Soon we passed the Seine, between St. Ouen and Asnières. We traversed the river a second time, leaving Argenteuil upon the left. We passed Sannois, Franconville, Eau-Bonne, St. Leu-Taverny, Villiers, and finally, Nesles. This was about twenty-seven miles from Paris, and we had reached this distance in two hours, although there was so little wind that the air scarcely stirred.

During the whole course of this delightful voyage, not the slightest apprehension for our fate or that of our machine entered my head for a moment. The globe did not suffer any alteration beyond the successive changes of dilatation and compression, which enabled us to mount and descend at will. The thermometer was, during more than an hour, between ten and twelve degrees above zero; this being to some extent accounted for by the fact that the interior of the car was warmed by the rays of the sun.

At the end of fifty-six minutes, we heard the report of the cannon which informed us that we had, at that moment, disappeared from view at Paris. We rejoiced that we had escaped, as we were no longer obliged to observe a horizontal course, and to regulate the balloon for that purpose. We gave ourselves up to the contemplation of the views which the immense stretch of country beneath us presented. From that time, though we had no opportunity of conversing with the inhabitants, we saw them running after us from all parts; we heard their cries, their exclamations of solicitude, and knew their alarm and admiration.

We cried, '*Vive le Roi!*' and the people responded. We heard, very distinctly—'My good friends, have you no fear? Are you not sick? How beautiful it is! Heaven preserve you! Adieu, my friends.'

I was touched to tears by this tender and true interest which our appearance had called forth.

We continued to wave our flags without cessation, and we perceived that these signals greatly increased the cheerfulness and calmed the solicitude of the people below. Often we descended sufficiently low to hear what they shouted to us. They asked us where we came from, and at what hour we had started.

We threw over successively frock-coats, muffs, and habits. Sailing on above the Ile d'Adam, after having admired the splendid view, we made signals with our flags, and demanded news of the Prince of Conti. One cried up to us, in a very powerful voice, that he was at Paris, and that he was ill. We regretted missing such an opportunity of paying

our respects, for we could have descended into the prince's gardens, if we had wished, but we preferred to pursue our course, and we re-ascended. Finally, we arrived at the plain of Nesles.

We saw from the distance groups of peasants, who ran on before us across the fields. 'Let us go,' I said, and we descended towards a vast meadow.

Some shrubs and trees stood round its border. Our car advanced majestically in a long inclined plane. On arriving near the trees, I feared that their branches might damage the car, so I threw over two pounds of ballast, and we rose again. We ran along more than 120 feet, at a distance of one or two feet from the ground, and had the appearance of travelling in a sledge. The peasants ran after us without being able to catch us, like children pursuing a butterfly in the fields.

Finally, we stopped, and were instantly surrounded. Nothing could equal the simple and tender regard of the country people, their admiration, and their lively emotion.

I called at once for the curés and the magistrates. They came round me on all sides: there was quite a fête on the spot. I prepared a short report, which the curés and the syndics signed. Then arrived a company of horsemen at a gallop. These were the Duke of Chartres, the Duke of Fitzjames, and M. Farrer. By a very singular chance, we had come down close by the hunting-lodge of the latter. He leaped from his horse and threw himself into my arms, crying, 'Monsieur Charles, I was first!'

We were both covered with the caresses of the prince, and I then narrated to him some incidents of the voyage.

'But this is not all, monseigneur.' I concluded 'I am going away again.'

'What! going away!' exclaimed the duke.

'Monseigneur, you will see. When do you wish me to come back again?'

'In half an hour.'

'Very well: be it so. In half an hour I shall be with you again.'

For his next experiment on December 1 1783 (opposite page), Professor Charles added a basket to his hydrogen balloon and ascended himself with one of his assistants. The two men took off from the Tuileries in Paris — their cords having been released by Montgolfier who was present among the vast crowds — landing an hour later at Nesle (above).

M. Robert descended from the car, and I was alone in the balloon.

I said to the duke, 'Monseigneur, I go.' I said to the peasants who held down the balloon, 'My friends, go away, all of you, from the car at the moment I give the signal.' I then rose like a bird, and in ten minutes I was more than 3,000 feet above the ground. I no longer perceived terrestrial objects; I only saw the great masses of nature.

I waited for what should happen. The balloon, which was quite flabby and soft when I ascended, was now taut, and fully distended. Soon the hydrogen gas began to escape in considerable quantities by the neck of the balloon, and then, from time to time, I pulled open the valve to give it two issues at once; and I continued thus to mount upwards, all the time losing the inflammable air, which, rushing past me from the neck of the balloon, felt like a warm cloud.

I passed in ten minutes from the temperature of spring to that of winter; the cold was keen and dry, but not insupportable. I examined all my sensations calmly; *I could hear myself live*, so to speak, and I am certain that at first I experienced nothing disagreeable in this sudden passage from one temperature to another.

When the barometer ceased to move I noted very exactly eighteen inches ten lines. This observation is perfectly accurate. The mercury did not suffer any sensible movement.

At the end of some minutes the cold caught my fingers; I could hardly hold the pen, but I no longer had need to do so. I was stationary, or rather moved only in a horizontal direction.

I raised myself in the middle of the car, and abandoned myself to the spectacle before me. At my departure from the meadow the sun had sunk to the people of the valleys; soon he shone for me alone, and came again to pour his rays upon the balloon and the car. I was the only creature in the horizon in sunshine—all the rest of nature was in shade. Ere long, however, the sun disappeared, and thus I had the pleasure of seeing him set twice in the same day. I contemplated for some moments the mists and vapours that rose from the valley and the rivers. The clouds seemed to come forth from the earth, and to accumulate the one upon the other. Their colour was a monotonous grey—a natural effect, for there was no light save that of the moon.

I observed that I had tacked round twice, and I felt currents which called me to my senses. I found with surprise the effect of the wind, and saw the cloth of my flag extended horizontally.

In the midst of the inexpressible pleasure of this state of ecstatic contemplation, I was recalled to myself by a most extraordinary pain which I felt in the interior of the ears and in the maxillary glands. This I attributed to the dilation of the air contained in the cellular tissue of the organ as much as to the cold outside. I was in my vest, with my head uncovered. I immediately covered my head with a bonnet of wool which was at my feet, but the pain only disappeared with my descent to the ground.

It was now seven or eight minutes since I had arrived at this elevation, and I now commenced to descend. I remembered the promise I had made to the Duke of Chartres, to return in half an hour. I quickened my descent by opening the valve from time to time. Soon the balloon, empty now to one half, presented the appearance of a hemisphere.

Arrived at twenty-three fathoms from the earth, I suddenly threw over two or three pounds of ballast, which arrested my descent, and which I had carefully kept for this purpose. I then slowly descended upon the ground, which I had, so to speak, chosen, and fulfilled my rendezvous with the prince.

On landing at Nesle, some 27 miles from Paris, Professor Charles and M. Robert were greeted by horsemen including the Duke of Chartres and the Duke of Fitzjames who had galloped in their wake from the capital. Professor Charles recounted their voyage briefly to the noblemen and their companions and then announced that he was going to ascend again on his own, promising to return in thirty minutes. The courageous aeronaut then asked those who held him down to let go and he rose into the skies again. In this subsequent voyage Professor Charles covered several more miles and in doing so became the first solo balloonist. Though he never ascended again afterwards, the contribution of this man of science to the art of ballooning was of the very first importance.

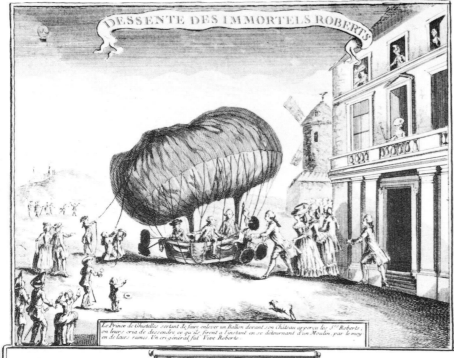

Perhaps one of the most hazardous of all the early balloon ascents was that led by Professor Charles' companion, M. Robert when he went up on July 15 1784 with his brother and the Duke of Chartres. The balloon for this journey was oblong in shape, sixty feet high and forty feet in diameter. However it was without a valve, the place of this being taken by a small globe filled with ordinary air inside the main balloon. This invention was based on a theory that when the balloon rose higher the hydrogen, being rarified, would compress the little globe within and press out of it a quantity of ordinary air equal to the amount of its dilation, thus correcting the height. The machine was also fitted with oars and a helm, but once in the air it began to spin around and the aeronauts quickly jettisoned these. They also found the small air balloon was not performing its function and the Duke was forced to slash it to release some air. The balloon then plunged to the ground and only the quick despatch of ballast prevented a disaster when it touched down. The journey had lasted less than five minutes. Four days later, however, the Robert Brothers had a rather more successful trip, as the second contemporary print shows, when they journeyed 159 miles from Paris to Bethune and were met on landing by the Prince of Ghistelles.

Traversing the Air in Balloons

Thomas Jefferson

Dr. Philip Turpin,
Chesterfield,
Virgina.

Annapolis, April 28, 1784

Dear Sir,

Supposing you may not have received intelligence to be relied on as to the reality & extent of the late discovery of traversing the air in balloons, & having lately perused a book in which everything is brought together on that subject as low down as Decemb. last, I will give you a detail of it. I will state the several experiments, with the most interesting circumstances attending them, by way of the table here which will give you a clearer view & in less compass.

They suppose the minimum of these balloons to be of 6 inches diameter: these are constructed of goldbeaters' skin & filled with inflammable air. This air produced from iron-filings, the vitriolic acid & distilled water is, in weight, to Atmospheric air as 7. to 43. on an average of the trials: & when produced from the filings of Zinc, the Marine acid & distilled water, is to the Atmospheric air as 5. to 53. or 1. to 10½. But Montgolfier's air is half the weight of Atmospheric, and this is produced by burning straw & wool. The straw must be dry & open, & the wool shred very fine, so that they may make a clear flame, with as little smoke as possible. 50 lb. of straw & 5 lb. of wool filled the ballons of Oct. 19. & Nov. 21. in five minutes. These ballons contained 60,000 cubic feet.

No analysis of this air is given, as Mons'r de Saintford, the author of the book, gives us a very great & useless display of Mathematical learning, which certainly has as yet had very little to do with this discovery: & when he comes to the chemical investigations, which are interesting, he says little. The ballons sometimes were torn by the pressure of the internal air being insufficiently counteracted in the higher regions of the Atmosphere. These rents were of 6. or 7. ft length, yet the machine descended with a gently equable motion & not with an accelerated one.

By the trials at Versailles & Champ de Mars it appears that they will go with a moderate wind 150. leagues in 24 hours. There are yet two principal *desiderata:*

(1) the cheapest & easiest process of making the lightest inflammable air and
(2) an envelopment which will be light, strong, impervious to the air & proof against rain.

Supplies of gas are desirable, too, without being obliged to carry fire with the machine: for in those in which men ascended there was a store of straw & wool laid in the gallery which surrounded the bottom of the balloon & in which the men stood, & a chaffing dish of 3 feet cube in which they burnt the materials to supply air.

It is conjectured that these machines may be guided by oars & raised & depressed by having vessels wherein, by the aid of pumps, they can produce a vacuum or condensation of atmospheric air at will. They are, from some new circumstances, strengthened in the opinion that there are generally opposite or different currents in the atmosphere: & that if the current next to the earth is not in the direction which suits you, by ascending higher you may find one that does. Between these there is probably a region of eddy where you may be stationary if philosophical experiments be your object.

The uses of this discovery are suggested to be:

(1) Transportation of commodities under some circumstances.
(2) Traversing deserts, countries possessed by an enemy, or ravaged by infectious disorders, pathless & inaccessible mountains.
(3) Conveying intelligence into a beseiged place, or perhaps enterprising on it, reconnoitring an army &c.
(4) Throwing new lights on the thermometer, barometer, hygrometer, rain, snow, hail, wind & other phenomena of which the Atmosphere is the theatre.
(5) The discovery of the pole which is but one day's journey in a balloon, from where the ice has hitherto stopped adventurers.
(6) Raising weights; lightening ships over bars.
(7) Housebreaking, smuggling &c.

Some of these objects are ludicrous, others serious, important and probable.

I trust that you will find all other figures relevant to the balloons in my table and understand their meaning to our future.

Be so good as to present my dutiful respects to my uncle & aunt & to be assured of the esteem with which I am Dr. Sir

your friend & serv't

Th: Jefferson

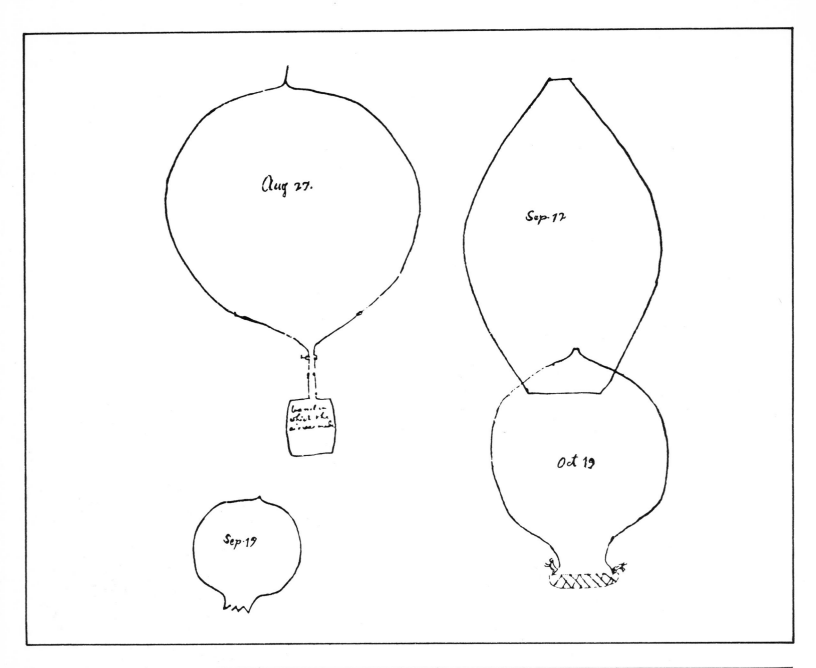

Date of experiment 1783	Place of experiment	Height of Ballon in feet	Diameter of Ballon in feet	Materials of which the Envelope was made	Materials from which the internal air was produced
June 5	Annonay		36	Paper	straw & wool burnt
Aug. 27	Champ de Mars		12	Taffety gum elastic	iron filings unindicated
Sept. 12	Academie Koiale	70		canvas and paper	straw & wool
Sept. 19	Versailles	57	41	cloth	straw & wool
Oct. 19	Paris	70	46		straw & wool
Nov. 21	Paris	70	46		

Moyen infaillible d'enlever les Ballons

Air de Pierrot

Voulez vous savoir le secret
De reussir dans l'aërostatique,
Avant que de vendre un billet,
Voyez ici comme l'on fait ?
Tout consiste dans la phisique
A raisonner et juger sainement.
Voila Messieurs et voila justement,
Comme on s'enleve facilement.

Air de Pierrot

Charles, Robert, les Mongolfiers
N'ont pas besoin de pareille rubrique,
Mais aussi ce sont des sorciers
Qu'auroient brulé nos devanciers.
Tout consiste dans la phisique
A raisonner et juger sainement.
Voila Messieurs et voila justement,
Comme on s'enleve facilement.

Se vend Paris rue des Quatre-vents

Drawn by R. Bonnington.

The *ASCENT* of M.ᴿ *S·ADLER* the celebrated *BRITISH AERONAUT* at *NOTTINGHAM* November 1ˢᵗ 1813

Published Jan.ʸ 17, 1814 by R. Bonnington Nottingham.

Although a carpenter named Wilcox had made a number of preliminary attempts at ballooning in America previously, the first aerial voyage took place on January 9 1793 at Philadelphia. The balloonist was the famed Frenchman, Jean Pierre Blanchard (1753-1809), the first 'professional' aeronaut, whose achievement was recorded in a contemporary illustration (above). The sketches are the work of Thomas Jefferson and reproduced from his letter. So, too, is the table of experiments reproduced across pages 36 and 39.

Weight comp'd with common air	Weight the Ballon could raise lbs	Horizontal distance to which it went	Ascent in the air	Miscellaneous circumstances
$\frac{1}{2}$	490	1200 toises	1000 toises	
1/6	35	5 leagues	unknown	
$\frac{1}{2}$	1250			
$\frac{1}{2}$	696	1700 toises	300 toises	a sheep, duck & cock aboard
$\frac{1}{2}$		50 toises	54 toises	2 men aboard
	1700	5000 toises in 20'	16000 toises	2 men aboard

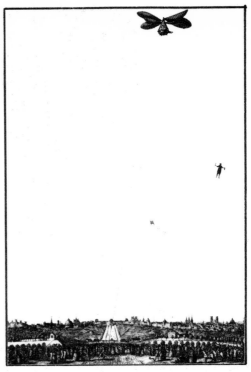

The balloon exploits of Blanchard have assured him a place in aeronautical history, but apart from virtually single-handedly introducing the art of aerostation to the American people (he exhibited his balloon widely but suffered a great deal from the attentions of hooligans who tried to destroy it) he also became the most popular balloonist in France during the closing years for the 18th Century. He is perhaps best known, though, for his extraordinary "Flying Ship"—a true Dream Machine if ever there was one! This craft resembled a sort of flying boat complete with oars and rigging and according to reports, Blanchard managed to sustain himself in it in the air for several minutes. During the year of 1782 the 'Flying Ship' was exhibited in a hotel garden in Paris, but immediately after the success of the Montgolfiers with their balloons the following year, Blanchard began working on a scheme to link his invention with that of the brothers. On March 2 1784 he brought his plans to fruition when, suspended beneath a balloon, his strange machine took to the skies from the Champ de Mars. The event came in for much comment from the caricaturists as the pictures here show. Unfortunately from Blanchard's point of view the voyage did prove that despite his persistence with oars they were of no real use in balloon navigation.

The following key to the numbers on the cut-away caricature of Blanchard's 'Flying Ship' are taken from a contemporary magazine:
1. Pedals in the form of levers; 2, Plyers in the form of levers: 3. Connecting lines which raise the pedals alternately; 4. Cords which serve to move the leading wings; 5. Travelling companion; 6. Pilot 7. Posts which support the top; 8. Supporting ropes which move the wings by means of pedals; 9. Connecting strings to prevent the

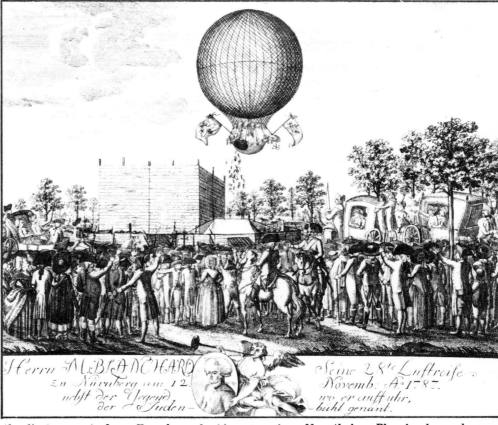

separation of the ropes; 10. Slides which prevent the displacement of the pedals and plyers; 11. Connecting cords which are attached under the pedals, and pass under the pulleys at the bottom of the keel; 12. Principal appliances for trimming the sails.

Blanchard, great showman that he was, not only ran risks from his balloon journeys but also at the hands of the general populace. Before making his great ascent on March 2 1784, a man named Dupont de Chambon tried to force himself on the aeronaut as a passenger and when denied permission, seized his sword and injured Blanchard, causing considerable damage to the balloon and delaying its departure (above left). In America as the next picture (top) shows, he gave the people of Gloucester County, New Jersey quite a scare when he alighted after his flight from Philadelphia. Fortunately the marksmen was restrained from putting a bullet through the

Frenchman by his companion . Nonetheless, Blanchard was always willing to travel far and near to exhibit his skill in the air and the third picture commemorates an ascent he made at Nurnberg in Germany on November 12, 1787. As he rises, the aeronaut is scattering leaflets to the onlookers announcing his futute ascents and their venues! Undoubtedly the highpoint of Blanchard's career was January 7, 1785, when he became the first man to cross the Channel from England to France. He was accompanied by an American physician, Dr. John Jeffries, who had financed the trip, and although somewhat of a hazardous crossing (at one point the two men had to throw everything overboard—including their clothes!—to avoid ditching in the sea) they did finally land twelve miles inland in the forest of Guînes. Needless to say both men were royally entertained by the delighted French.

A Despatch from the Devil's Horse

Vincent Lunardi

In England, the first balloon voyage was to be successfully accomplished in 1784 by an Italian aeronaut, Vincent Lunardi (1759-1806). Lunardi's extraordinary and daring exploits in the air made him a popular hero throughout Europe and his self-confessed acts of showmanship make this not a difficult fact to understand!

R.^d Cosway delineavi.   F. Bartolozzi Sculp.^t

-- et se
Protinùs ætherea tollit inastra via.

VINCENT LUNARDI ESQ.^r

*Secretary to the Neapolitan Ambassador
and the first aerial Traveller in the
English Atmosphere
Septr 15. 1784*

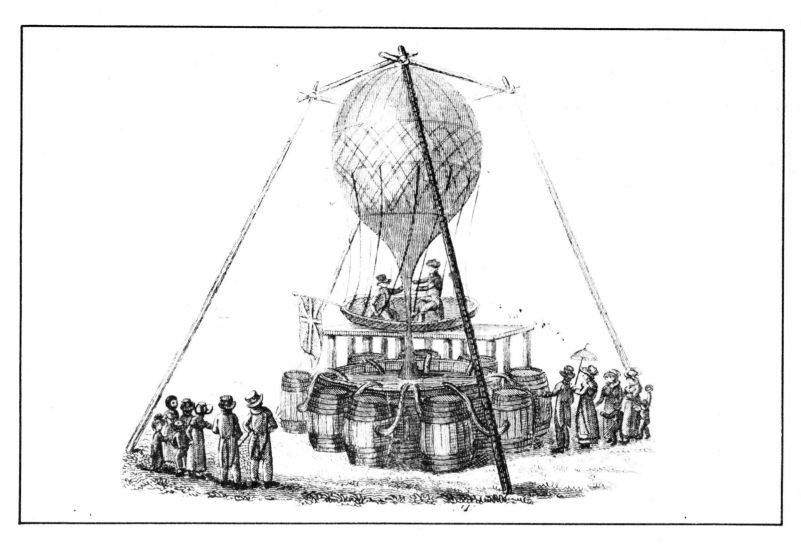

At last the final gun was fired, the cords divided, and the Balloon rose, thus beginning the first aerial voyage in England. The effect was that of a miracle on the multitudes which surrounded the place and I had recourse to every stratagem to let them know I was in the gallery, and they literally rent the air with their acclamations and applause. In these stratagems I devoted my flag, and worked with my oars, one of which was immediately broken, and fell from me. A pigeon, too, escaped, which, with a dog, and cat, were the only companions of my excursion.

When the thermometer had fallen from 68° to 61° I perceived a great difference in the temperature of the air. I became very cold, and found it necessary to take a few glasses of wine. I likewise ate the leg of a chicken, but my bread and other provisions had been rendered useless, by being mixed with the sand, which I carried as ballast.

When the thermometer was at 50° the effect of the atmosphere, and the combination of circumstances around, produced a calm delight, which is inexpressible, and no situation on earth could give. The stillness, extent, and magnificence of the scene, rendered it highly awful. My horizon seemed a perfect circle; the terminating line several hundred miles in circumference. This I conjectured from the view of London; the extreme points of which, formed an angle of only a few degrees. It was so reduced on the great scale before me, that I can find no simile to convey any idea of it. I could distinguish St. Paul's and other churches, from the houses. I saw the streets as lines, all animated with beings, whom I knew to be men and women, but which I should otherwise have had a difficulty in describing. It was an enormous bee-hive, but the industry of it was suspended. All the moving mass seemed to have no object but myself, and the transition from the suspicion, and perhaps contempt of the preceding hour, to the affectionate transport, admiration and glory of the present moment, was not without its effect on my mind. I recollected the puns* on my name, and was glad to find myself calm. I had soared from the apprehensions and anxieties of the Artillery Ground, and felt as if I had left behind me all the cares and passions that molest mankind.

Indeed, the whole scene before me filled the mind with a sublime pleasure, of which I never had a conception. The critics imagine, for they seldom speak from experience, that terror is an ingredient in every sublime sensation. It was not profitable for me to be on earth, in a situation so free from apprehension. I had not the slightest sense of motion from the Machine, I knew not whether it went swiftly or slowly, whether it ascended or descended, whether it was agitated or tranquil, but by the appearance or disappearance of objects on the earth. I moved to different parts of the gallery, I adjusted the furniture, and apparatus. I uncorked my bottle, ate, drank, and wrote, just as in my study. The height had not the effect, which a much lesser degree of it has near the earth, that of producing giddiness. The broomsticks of the witches, Ariostos's flying horse, and even Milton's fun beam conveying the angel to earth, have all an idea of effort, difficulty, and restraint, which do not affect a voyage in the Balloon.

Thus tranquil, and thus situated, how shall I describe to you a view, such as the ancients supposed Jupiter to have of earth, and to copy which there are no terms in any language. The gradual diminution of objects, and the masses of light and shade are intelligible in oblique and common prospects. But here everything wore a new appearance, and had a new effect. The face of the country had a mild and permanent verdure, to which Italy is a stranger. The variety of cultivation, and the accuracy with which property is divided, give the idea ever present to a stranger in England, of good civil laws and an equitable administration: the rivers meandering; the sea glisening with the rays of the sun; the immense district beneath me spotted with cities, towns, villages, and houses, pouring out their inhabitants to hail my appearance: you will allow me some merit at not having been exceedingly intoxicated with my situation.

* In some of the papers, witticisms appeared on the affinity of, Lunatic & Lunardi.

To prolong my enjoyment of it, and to try the effect of my only oar, I kept myself in the same parallel respecting the earth, for nearly half an hour. But the exercise having fatigued, and the experience having satisfied me, I laid aside my car, and again had recourse to my bottle; this I emptied to the health of my friends and benefactors in the lower world. All my affections were alive, in a manner not easily to be conceived, and you may be assured that the sentiment which seemed to me most congenial to that happy situation was gratitude and friendship. I will not refer to any softer passion. I sat down and wrote four pages of desultory observations, and pinning them to a napkin, committed them to the mild winds of the region, to be conveyed to my honoured friend and patron, Prince Caramanico.

During this business I had ascended rapidly; for, on hearing the report of a gun, fired in the Artillery Ground, I was induced to examine the thermometer, and found it had fallen to 32°. The Balloon was so much inflated as to assume the form of an oblong spheroid, the shortest diameter of which was in a line with me,

though I had ascended with it in the shape of an inverted cone, and wanted nearly one third of its full compliment of air. Having no valve, I could only open the neck of the Balloon; thinking it barely possible that the strong ratefaction might force out some of the inflammable air. The condensed vapour around its neck was frozen, though I found no inconveniences from the cold. The earth, at this point, appeared like a boundless plain, whose surface had variegated shades, but on which no object could be accurately distinguished.

I then had recourse to the utmost use of my single oar; by hard and persevering labour I brought myself within three hundred yards of the earth, and moving horizontally, spoke through my trumpet to some country people, from whom I heard a confused noise in reply.

At half after three o'clock, I descended in a corn field, on the common of South Mimms, where I landed the cat. The poor animal had been sensibly affected by the cold, during the greatest part of the voyage. Here I might have terminated my excursion with satisfaction and

honour to myself; for though I was not destitute of ambition, to be the first to ascend the English atmosphere, my great object was to ascertain the effect of oars, acting vertically on the air. I had lost one of my oars, but by the use of the other, I had brought myself down, and was perfectly convinced my invention would answer. This, though a single, was an important object, and my satisfaction was very great in having proved its utility. The fatigues and anxiety I have endured, might have induced me to be content with what I had done, and the people about me were very ready to assist at my disembarkation, but my affections were afloat, and in unison with the whole country, whose transport and admiration seemed boundless. I bid them therefore keep clear, and I would gratify them by ascending directly in their view.

My general course to this place was something more than one point to the westward of north. A Gentleman on horseback approached me, but I could not speak to him, being intent on my re-ascension, which I affected, after moving horizontally about forty yards. As I ascended, one of the ballustrades of the gallery gave way; but the circumstance excited no apprehension of danger. I threw out the remainder of my ballast and provisions, and again resumed my pen. My ascension was so rapid, that before I had written half a page, the thermometer had fallen to 29°. The drops of water that adhered to the neck of the Balloon were become like crystals. At this point of elevation, which was the highest I attained, I finished my letter, and fastening it with a cork-screw to my handkerchief, threw it down. I likewise threw down the plates, knives and forks, the little sand that remained, and an empty bottle, which took some time in disappearing. I now wrote the last of my dispatches from the clouds, which I fixed to a leathern belt, and sent towards the earth. It was visible to me on its passage for several minutes, but I myself was insensible of motion from the machine itself, during the whole voyage. The earth appeared as before, like an extensive plain, with the same variegated surface; but the objects rather less distinguishable. The clouds to the eastward rolled beneath me, in masses immensely larger than the waves of an ocean. I therefore did not mistake them for the sea. Contrasted with the effects of the sun on the earth and water beneath, they gave a grandeur to the whole scene which no fancy can describe. I again betook myself to my oar, in order to descend; and by the hard labour of fifteen or twenty minutes I accomplished my design, when my strength was nearly exhausted. My principal care was to avoid a violent concussion at landing, and in this good fortune was my friend.

At twenty minutes past four I descended in a spacious meadow, in the parish of Standon, near Ware, in Hertfordshire. Some labourers were at work in it. I requested their assistance; they exclaimed they would have nothing to do with one who came in the Devil's house, or on the Devil's horse (I could not distinguish which of the phrases they used) and no intreaties could prevail on them to approach me.

I at last owed my deliverance to the spirit and generosity of a female. A young woman, who was likewise in the field, took hold of a cord which I had thrown out, and calling to the men, they yielded that assistance to her request which they had refused to mine. A crowd of people from the neighbourhood soon assembled, who very obligingly assisted me to disembark. The inflammable air was then let out by an incision and produced a most offensive stench, which is said to have affected the atmosphere of the entire neighbourhood!

September 15, 1784

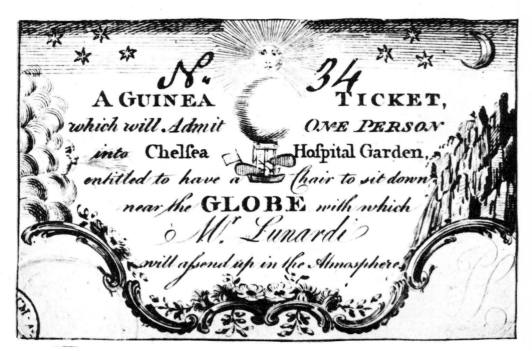

GRAND ENGLISH BALLOON.
To the Nobility, Gentry, and Public in general.
A LARGE AND CURIOUS
BALLOON
IS NOW CONSTRUCTING AT THE
LYCEUM near EXETER-CHANGE, STRAND,
ON A PLAN ENTIRELY NOVEL,
And which has originated in this METROPOLIS,
FROM THE INGENUITY OF A
GENTLEMAN,
WHO IS TO ASCEND WITH IT.

The Conftruction is now begun at the above Place, and when the GLOBE (the Materials of which are oiled Silk of different Colours) is completed, it will be filled with Inflammable Air, and launched from

Chelfea Hofpital Gardens,
Having obtained Permiffion for that Purpofe.
The Object of the Gentleman's Ærial Tour is to make fome interefting Experiments, by which it is prefumed this Nation will difcover its real Utility.
THE GALLERY, OARS AND WINGS ARE NOW FINISHED.
SUBSCRIPTIONS are received at the OFFICE adjoining to the LYCEUM, where TICKETS may be had.
ONE GUINEA Ticket will admit a Perfon Four different Times, to fee the Conftruction, and likewife into the Garden, intitled to have a Chair near the GLOBE to fee it launched off.
A HALF GUINEA Ticket will admit a Perfon to fee the Conftruction Twice, and likewife into the Garden, intitled to have a proper Bench to fit down on, next to the above Subfcribers.
FIVE SHILLING Tickets will admit a Perfon Once to fee the Conftruction, and likewife into the Garden to have a proper Bench to fit down on.
The above ROOM is now open from TEN o'Clock till EIGHT o'Clock, for the Admiffion of SUBSCRIBERS, where the CONSTRUCTION, GALLERY, OARS, and WINGS, together with other BALLOONS may be feen.
Admittance for Non-Subfcribers Two Shilling and Six-pence each.

Printed by J. P. COGHLAN, in Duke-Street near Grofvenor-Square.

N° 34 A GUINEA TICKET, which will Admit ONE PERSON into Chelfea Hofpital Garden, entitled to have a Chair to sit down near the GLOBE with which Mr. Lunardi will afcend up in the Atmofphere.

The first aerial voyage in England was made on September 15, 1784 by the handsome and dashing secretary to the Neapolitan Embassy in London, Vincent Lunardi. The journey proceeded from Moorfields in London to Standon near Ware in Hertfordshire where the spot is now marked with a plaque. In subsequent years Lunardi made several further ascents in England and reproduced here are a typical poster and admission ticket relating to these events.

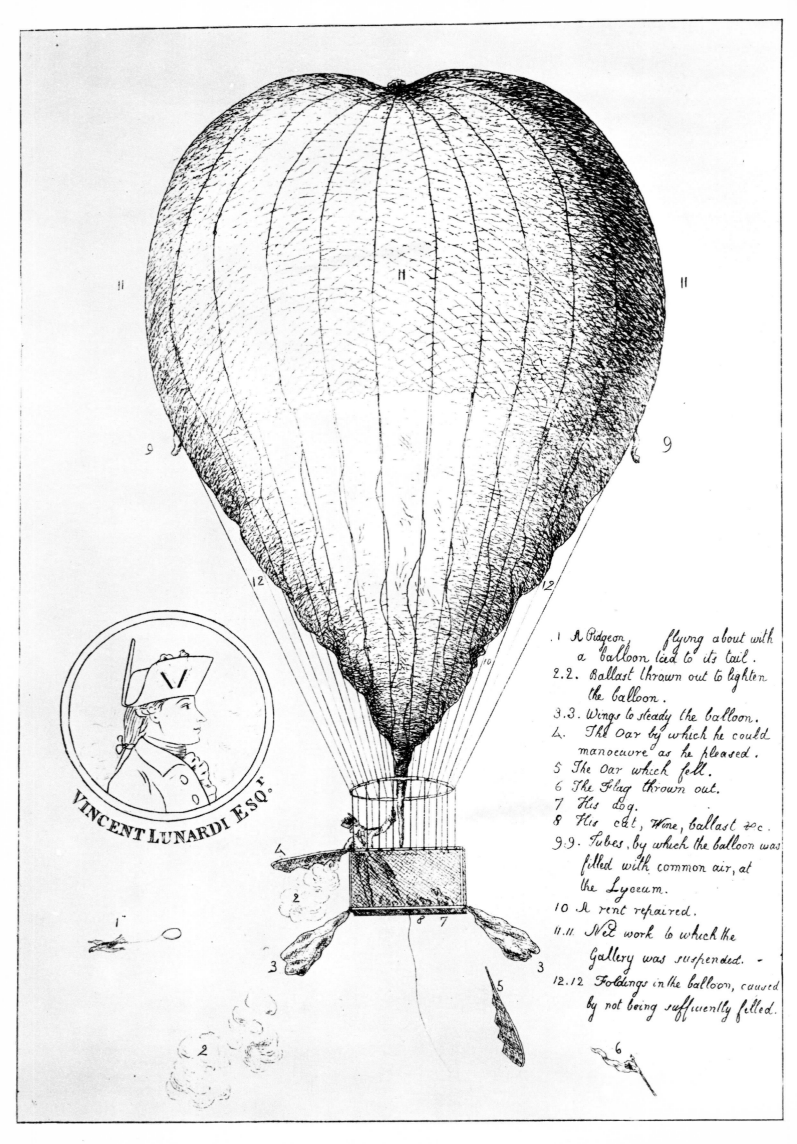

VINCENT LUNARDI ESQ.

1. A Pidgeon, flying about with a balloon tied to its tail.
2.2. Ballast thrown out to lighten the balloon.
3.3. Wings to steady the balloon.
4. The Oar by which he could manoeuvre as he pleased.
5. The Oar which fell.
6. The Flag thrown out.
7. His dog.
8. His cat, Wine, ballast &c.
9.9. Tubes, by which the balloon was filled with common air, at the Lyceum.
10. A rent repaired.
11.11. Net work to which the Gallery was suspended.
12.12. Foldings in the balloon, caused by not being sufficiently filled.

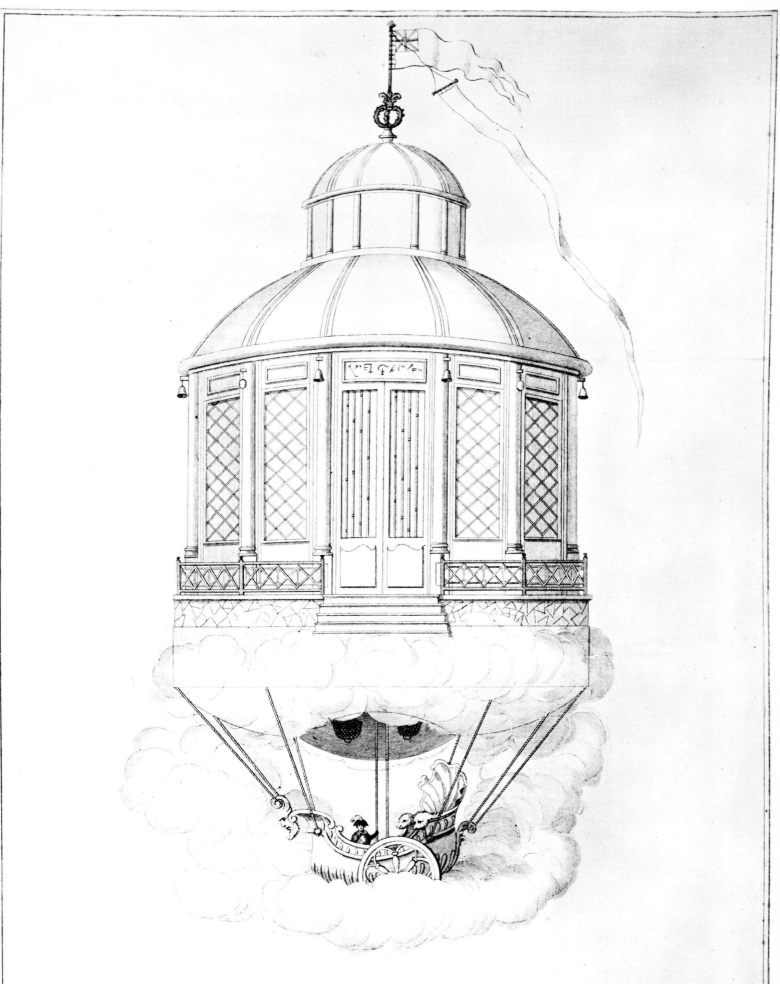

NEW AEROSTATIC MACHINE,

Being 65 Feet High, and 120 in Circumference, in which M. Le Chev. de Moret will go up

the of May 1784.

A Tale of Terror

Thomas Hood

"A Tale of Terror" is one of the very earliest pieces of fiction about ballooning and certainly the first short story. Thomas Hood (1799-1845) was one of the great humourists of his age and also a novelist of no mean repute—"Eugene Aram" being perhaps his most famous work.

The following story I had from the lips of a well-known Aeronaut, and nearly in the same words.

It was on one of my ascents from Vauxhall, and a gentleman of the name of Mavor had engaged himself as a companion in my aerial excursion. But when the time came his nerves failed him, and I looked vainly round for the person who was to occupy the vacant seat in the car. Having waited for him till the last possible moment, and the crowd in the gardens becoming impatient, I prepared to ascend alone; and the last cord that attached me to the earth was about to be cast off, when suddenly a strange gentleman pushed forward and volunteered to go up with me into the clouds. He pressed the request with so much earnestness that, having satisfied myself, by a few questions, of his respectability and received his promise to submit in every point to my directions, I consented to receive him in lieu of the absentee; whereupon he stepped with evident eagerness and alacrity into the machine. In another minute we were rising above the trees; and in justice to my companion I must say, that in all my experience no person at a first ascent had ever shown such perfect coolness and self-possession. The sudden rise of the

machine, the novelty of the situation, the real and exaggerated dangers of the voyage, and the cheering of the spectators are apt to cause some trepidation, or at any rate excitement, in the boldest individuals; whereas the stranger was as composed and comfortable as if he had been sitting quiet at home in his own library chair. A bird could not have seemed more at ease, or more in its element, and yet he solemnly assured me, upon his honour, that he had never been up before in his life. Instead of exhibiting any alarm at our great height from the earth, he evinced the liveliest pleasure whenever I emptied one of my bags of sand, and even once or twice urged me to part with more of the ballast. In the meantime, the wind, which was very light, carried us gently along in a north-east direction, and the day being particularly bright and clear, we enjoyed a delightful bird's-eye view of the great metropolis and the surrounding country. My companion listened with great interest while I pointed out to him the various objects over which we passed, till I happened casually to observe that the balloon must be directly over Hoxton. My fellow-traveller then for the first time betrayed some uneasiness, and anxiously inquired whether I thought he could be recognised by anyone at our then distance from the earth. It was, I told him, quite impossible. Nevertheless he continued very uneasy, frequently repeating, "I hope they don't see," and entreating me earnestly to discharge more ballast. It then flashed upon me for the first time that his offer to ascend with me had been a whim of the moment, and that he feared being seen at that perilous elevation

Danger was never far away for the pioneer aeronauts as these two illustrations, separated by nearly one hundred years, clearly show. In the first (above), the French balloonist Rodez and his companion are coming to grief in some trees, on August 6 1784. In the second (opposite), the great American balloonist, John La Mountain, who played such an important role in the use of balloons in the Civil War and several times tried to set up a project for crossing the Atlantic by balloon, is seen about to plunge to his death during a special ascent made on Independence Day, July 4 1873.

by any member of his own family. I therefore asked him if he resided at Hoxton, to which he replied in the affirmative; urging again, and with great vehemence, the emptying of the remaining sandbags.

This, however, was out of the question, considering the altitude of the balloon, the course of the wind, and the proximity of the sea-coast. But my comrade was deaf to these reasons; he insisted on going higher, and on my refusal to discharge more ballast deliberately pulled off and threw his hat, coat, and waistcoat overboard.

"Hurrah, that lightened her!" he shouted; "but it's not enough yet," and he began unloosening his cravat.

"Nonsense," said I, "my good fellow, nobody can recognise you at this distance, even with a telescope."

"Don't be too sure of that," he retorted rather simply; "they have sharp eyes at Miles's."

"At where?"

"At Miles's Madhouse!"

Gracious Heaven!—the truth flashed upon me in an instant. I was sitting in the frail car of a balloon, at least a mile above the earth, with a Lunatic! The horrors of the situation, for a minute, seemed to deprive me of my own senses. A sudden freak of a distempered fancy, a transient fury, the slightest struggle might send us both, at a moment's notice, into eternity! In the meantime the Maniac, still repeating his insane cry of "higher, higher, higher," divested himself, successively, of every remaining article of clothing, throwing each portion, as soon as taken off, to the winds. The inutility of remonstrance, or rather the probability of its producing a fatal irritation, keep me silent during these operations: but judge of my terror when, having thrown his stockings overboard, I heard him say, "We are not yet high enough by ten thousand miles—one of us must throw out the other."

To describe my feelings at this speech is impossible. Not only the awfulness of my position, but its novelty, conspired to bewilder me, for certainly no flight of imagination—no, not the wildest nightmare dream—had ever placed me in so desperate and forlorn a situation. It was horrible, horrible! Words, pleadings, remonstrances were useless, and resistance would be certain destruction. I had better have been unarmed, in an American Wilderness, at the mercy of a savage Indian! And now, without daring to stir a hand in opposition, I saw the Lunatic deliberately heave first one and then the other bag of ballast from the car, the balloon, of course, rising with proportionate rapidity. Up, up, up it soared—to an altitude I had never even dared to contemplate; the earth was lost to my eyes, and nothing but the huge clouds rolled beneath us! The world was gone, I felt, for ever! The Maniac, however, was still dissatisfied with our ascent, and again began to mutter.

"Have you a wife and children?" he asked abruptly.

Prompted by a natural instinct, and with a pardonable deviation from truth, I replied that I was married, and had fourteen young ones who depended on me for their bread!

"Ha! ha! ha!" laughed the Maniac, with a sparkling of his eyes that chilled my very marrow. "I have three hundred wives and five thousand children; and if the balloon had not been so heavy by carrying double, I should have been home to them by this time."

"And where do they live?" I asked, anxious to gain time by any question that first occurred to me.

"In the moon," replied the Maniac; "and when I have lightened the car, I shall be there in no time!"

(Thomas Hood's story ends abruptly at this point and despite frequent requests which were made to him after its initial publication, he never added to it further—leaving the reader to make his own mind up about the outcome of the terrifying situation. Editor's note.)

Three other pictures which also illustrate some remarkable ballooning escapes. In the first (opposite) the Frenchman Duruof managed to survive a plunge to earth after his tethered balloon, "Le Neptune" exploded in 1860. Not long deterred by this narrow escape from death he was soon in the skies again and then on September 1 1873 had an even more miraculous escape when his new balloon, "Tricolore", came down in the North Sea (top). On this occasion he was accompanied by his wife and fortunately a fishing boat spotted their fall and rescued them from a watery grave. In the third picture, a group of English aeronauts find themselves ascending unexpectedly while filling their balloon from a gas holder (a much used source of supply over the years.) However, they were able to get the craft under control and land safely much to the relief of the assistant still clutching the guide ropes.

The poster provides a salutary reminder that the show must always go on despite man, balloon or the elements!

Descent by Parachute

Andre Garnerin

Balloons were to play a major part in the development of the parachute and again it was a Frenchman, André Garnerin (1769-1823) who devised and demonstrated the first one. In this account he modestly reports a descent, and one cannot help feeling he understates the very real courage it must have taken to leap out of the balloon's basket. Sadly, Garnerin was killed experimenting with a parachute—but he bequeathed to aviation the means whereby so many lives have since been saved.

The experiment of my thirty-first ascent, and of my new descent in a parachute, took place in London on a very fine day, and in the presence of an immense crowd of spectators, who filled the streets, windows, and houses, and the scaffoldings erected around the place of my departure, which, alas! was the only spot not crowded with spectators!

It is necessary, when I undertake the experiment of the parachute, that I should know the state of the atmosphere, in order to enable me to judge of the course I am to take; and also to adopt the precautions to ensure success. About three in the afternoon, I had the satisfaction of having a first indication from the agreeable effect of a very pretty Montgolfier balloon, which was sent off from the environs of St. George's Parade, and which took a direction over Marylebone.

The success of this experiment ought not to prevent me from expressing my opinion of the dangers that may result to the general safety from the daily abuse of those night experiments, which are not always directed by persons conversant with the subject. One shudders when one thinks, that a machine of this kind may fall, and fall on fire, upon the cordage of a ship, and thus involve in one great conflagration, all that constitutes the wealth of one of the first cities in the world. The use of these machines was prohibited in France; and the Consular Government confided to me alone the direction of night balloons, which I conceived and introduced into the national fetes.

Convinced of the direction of the wind, I hastened the filling of the balloon, and at five P.M. I filled the pilot balloon which Mrs. Sheridan did me the honour to launch. It seemed to me that I was conciliating the favour of Heaven by the interference of the graces. This pilot balloon ascended quickly, and was soon out of sight, marking out my career towards the North-east. Whilst the anxious crowd were following the path of my little pilot, I suspended my parachute to the balloon: this painful and difficult operation was executed with all possible address, by the assistance of the most distinguished personages. The parachute was gradually suspended, and the breeze, which was very gentle, did not produce the least obstacle. At length I hastened to ballast my cylindrical bark, and to place myself in it; a sight which the public contemplated with deep interest—it seemed at that moment as if every heart beat in unison; for, though I have not the advantage of speaking English, every one understands my signs. I ascertained the height of the barometer, which was at 29½ inches. I now pressed the moment of my departure, and the period of fulfilling my engagements with the British public.

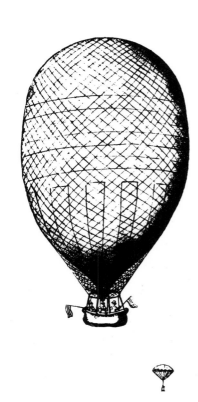

Ascended from Ranelagh on Monday, June 28th, 1802, with M. Garnerin and Capt. Snowden, & descended four Miles beyond Colchester in Essex, a distance of Sixty Miles, which they accomplish'd (the Wind being uncommonly High,) in 45 Minutes. The greatest Height they attain'd was 10,000 Feet.

Ascended from Vauxhall Gardens on Tuesday, Aug'st 3, 1802, with M. Garnerin, Madame Garnerin, and M'r Glassford. The Weather being extremely fine M. Garnerin, when at the Height of 200 Fathoms, launch'd a Cat with a Parachute in Miniature, when they had travers'd the Air sixty two Minutes, they descended in Lord Rosslyns Paddock, on the Top of Hampstead Hill, Middlesex, 4 Miles from London. Their greatest Distance from the Earth was 2400 Feet.

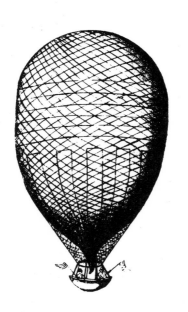

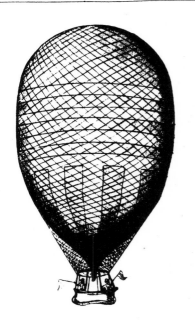

Ascended from Lord's Cricket Ground, Marylebone, on Monday, July 5, 1802, with Miss Garnerin and Locker, the Weather being extremely wet and cloudy, they in three Minutes became invisible, & in a quarter of an Hour descended at Changford Green, in Essex a distance of Miles. The greatest Height they attain'd was 7,800 Feet.

Ascended from St George's Parade, North Audley Street, on Tuesday Sept 21 1802, with M. Garnerin who when at the Height of 8000 Feet made his Descent with a Parachute, & safely descended in a Field between St Pancras Church, and the Small Pox Hospital, London. He was precisely 10 Minutes & 20 Seconds in making the Descent. The first ever made in England by a Parachute.

Ascended from Sydney Gardens Bath on Tuesday Sept 7, 1802, with M. Garnerin accompanied by M'r Glassford who ascended from Vauxhall. The Day being propitious they continued their arial Voyage for an Hour & 50 Minutes & then descended in a Field near Melle Park, the Seat of T'r Horner Esq'r 16 Miles from Bath. The greatest elevation they attain'd was 5420 Feet.

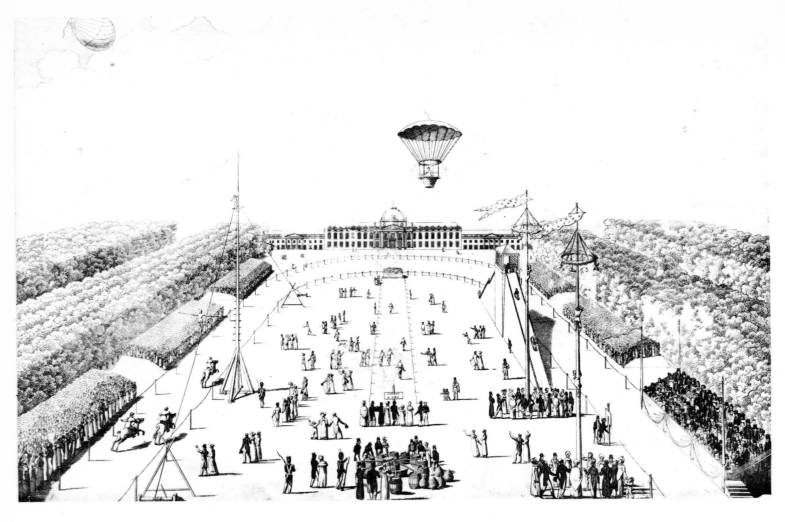

Mr. & Madme Garnerin

as they appeared Aug. 5th 1802 at Vauxhall, taken by a Gentleman present at the time. The Balloon is an exact Copy.

Andre Garnerin was the creator of the parachute and demonstrated his invention for the first time to the people of Monceau on October 22 1797. He ascended in a balloon and on reaching the height of 2,000 feet cut the cord which linked him to the aerostat and plunged to earth. The huge crowd which had assembled at first feared for his life, but as his fall slowed down and he gently descended onto the plain their alarm changed to delight and applause. France had again been first in an aeronautical discovery.

All the cords were cut; I rose amidst the most expressive silence, and, launching into infinite space, discovered from on high the countless multitude that sent up their sighs and prayers for my safety. My parachute in form of a doom over my head, had a majestic effect. I quickened my ascending impulse, and rose through light and thin vapours where the cold informed me that I was entering into the upper region. I followed attentively the route I was taking and perceived that I had reached the extremity of the city, and that immense fields and meadows offered themselves for my descent. I examined my barometer, which I found fallen to 23 inches—the sky was clear, the moment favourable, and I threw down my flag to endeavour to shew to the people assembled that I was on the point of cutting the cord that suspended me between heaven and earth. I made every necessary disposition prepared my ballast, and measured with my eye the vast space that separated me from the rest of the human race. I felt my courage confirmed by the certainty that my combinations were just. I then took out my knife *and with a hand firm, from a conscience void of reproach, and which had never been lifted against any one but in the field of victory*, I cut the cord.

My balloon rose, and I felt myself precipitated with a velocity which was checked by the sudden unfolding of my parachute. I saw that all my calculations were just, and my mind remained calm and serene. I endeavoured to modulate my gravitation, and the oscillation which I experienced increased in proportion as I approached the breeze that blows in the middle regions; nearly ten minutes had elapsed, and I felt that the more time I took in descending the safer I should reach the ground. At length I perceived thousands of people, some on horseback; others on foot, following me, all of whom encouraged me by their wishes, while they opened their arms to receive me. I came near the earth, and, after one bound, I landed and quitted the parachute, without any shock or accident.

The first person that came to me pressed me in his arms; but without loosing any time, I employed myself in detaching the principal circle of the parachute, anxious to

54

n Exact Reprefentation of Mr LUNARDI's Grand Air Balloon

Ascending from the Artillery Ground, London, Septr 15. 1784.

The fatal Descent of the Parachute by which
Mr. Cocking lost his life.

Mr. COCKING.

The Ascent of the Royal Nassau Balloon from Vauxhall,
with the Parachute attached.

THE ONLY AUTHENTIC SKETCH OF THE ASCENT OF THE

VAUXHALL BALLOON WITH Mr COCKING'S PARACHUTE.

Distance of the top of the Balloon from
the Parachute 50 feet
Diameter of the Parachute 35 feet

The Streamer from the Balloon was a
canvas tube for throwing out Ballast.

WITH A SKETCH OF THE FATAL DESCENT OF Mr COCKING.

Garnerin also made the first parachute descent in England, in 1802, and among his audience was a young painter named Robert Cocking who felt there must be a way of eliminating the oscillation which made it so uncomfortable to use. Some thirty five years later, on July 24 1837, he believed he had perfected his design and asked to be taken up from the Vauxhall Gardens, London to try it out. Unfortunately for Cocking his calculations proved to be incorrect and disaster followed.

save the instrument that had so well guaranteed me; but a crowd soon surrounded me—laid hold of me, and carried me in triumph, till an indisposition, the consequence and effect of the oscillation I had experienced, obliged the procession to stop. I was then seized with a painful vomiting, which I usually experience for several hours after a descent in a parachute.

The interval of a moment, however, permitting me to get on horseback; a numerous cavalcade approached to keep off the crowd, whose enthusiasm and transports incommoded me not a little. The Duke of York was among the horsemen; and the procession proceeded with great difficulty in the midst of the crowd, who shouted forth their applause, and had before them the tri-coloured flag which I had thrown down, and which was carried by a

member of Parliament. Among the prodigious concourse of persons on foot, I remarked Lord Stanhope, from whom I had received the councils of a scientific man, and who penetrated through the crowd to shake hands with me. At length, after several incidents, all produced by the universal interest with which I was honoured, I withdrew from the crowd without any other accident than that of having my right foot jammed between the horse I rode and a horseman who pressed too close to me. My parachute was preserved as well as could be expected, a few of the cords only were cut. It is now exhibiting at the Pantheon, where a great concourse of persons have been to examine it.

There is a chasm in the report which I have given of my descent in a parachute, upon which I have had several questions put to me: it is the explanation of the cause which gave rise to the great oscillation which my parachute experienced. Several persons imagined that an accident had happened to the parachute: others, and the greater number, though that I had not ballast enough in my car, which would have preserved the equilibrium, and have made the car gravitate better. I was myself of this latter opinion during the first part of my descent; but a thing may be probable, and yet not true. I will endeavour to throw some light upon the subject:

We must consider, that the experiment of the parachute is founded upon the elasticity of the air, whose relation is always in a direct ratio with the weight that compresses it; when once the air has been condensed relative to the weight that compresses it, it maintains itself constantly in

When the balloon with Cocking and his parachute suspended below had reached 5,000 feet, the inventor operated his release gear and fell free. Sadly he had not allowed for the wind pressure and this caused the ribs of the parachute to crack as it careered down and the whole assembly and its unfortunate passenger were smashed to pieces in a field at Lee Green.

that situation, and cannot depart from it without an addition to, or subtraction from, the compressing force. Hence it follows, that a parachute, which should be perfect in its construction, and which should preserve its state of equilibrium, (a thing physically impossible) would remain for ever stationary, upon the column of air which it compressed, without ever ascending or descending. A parachute, therefore, cannot descend, but by the evaporation of the air.

The slightest cause may give the first impulse to these evaporations, which, once having taken place, continue in torrents, and with a greater degree of rapidity in proportion as the compressing weight is more considerable. The wind which acts upon the surface of the parachute, or the slightest movement of posture of the person in the car, or both these causes at once, (without speaking of the imperfection of the parachute itself) must produce a first inclination, which is soon followed by a second, in an opposite direction, by the effort made by the weight contained in the car, to return to the centre of gravity. This first oscillation, once established, is incessantly kept up by the evaporation of the air, and increases as the compressing force, or the weight suspended to the parachute excites it to do it with rapidity. The following is the proof which justifies this reasoning:

When I made my first experiments of descending in a parachute, I always made use of a balloon proportioned to the weight which I was to carry up; and I took with me a sack of ballast of only twenty pounds, which I threw out with one hand while I cut the cord of separation with the other. The balloon being this time much larger, I wished to make use of its size and energies to sound the capacity of my parachute. Instead of twenty pounds of ballast, I carried upwards of one hundred; I threw out only a small part the moment I was separated from the balloon, and the oscillations having commenced almost immediately with very great rapidity, I thought that my parachute was tossed about by a sudden breeze. I then erroneously reasoned that the more ballast I threw out, the more I should diminish the power that tended to restore the equilibrium. I did not imagine that the air being compressed by a weight twice greater almost than in my former experiments, the evaporation would take place with a relative reaction.

When I was no more than a few hundred feet high, I saw clearly that I should be dashed to pieces, if I touched the ground during the operation of an oscillation. The man that is collected in danger always finds resources which do not enter the conception of a man who loses his recollection. Nature having favoured me in this respect, I have always escaped the greatest dangers, particularly in the army. I saw what was proper to be done, and immediately threw out all that was in the car, even to my barometer, which, by the way, has never been restored. The effect justified my expectations; all the violent oscillations ceased in a moment, and those which succeeded were much less rapid, and their extent comparatively trifling. I then felt that sensation in the stomach which produced the vomitting I experienced when I got out of the car.

I infer, from what I have stated before, that the greater the surface of the parachute is, and the less it is loaded, the lighter the descent will be; and the more uniform, and free from those oscillations, caused by the evaporation of the compressed air; the counterpoise caused by a fresh wind, which should act upon the surface of the parachute, would be little to be feared. We are furnished with daily proofs by the little parachutes which children launch in the streets with wonderful address. The weight they support is nothing almost, when compared with the extent of the surface of the sheet of paper. Hence these little parachutes take a horizontal course, sometimes for a long time without oscillation, though the wind even be high, or at least, the oscillations they do experience are slow, and not violent, and only become considerable when gusts of wind blow at the corner of the streets.

The "Monstre" Balloon

Thomas Ingoldsby

"The Ingoldsby Legends or Mirth & Marvels" (1840) is one of the gems of English humour and it is perhaps not surprising to find that with the great interest in ballooning, the author included an item devoted to this art. Richard Barham (1788—1845) who as 'Thomas Ingoldsby' wrote the "Legends" was a balloon enthusiast and an associate of several of the noted aeronauts of the time.

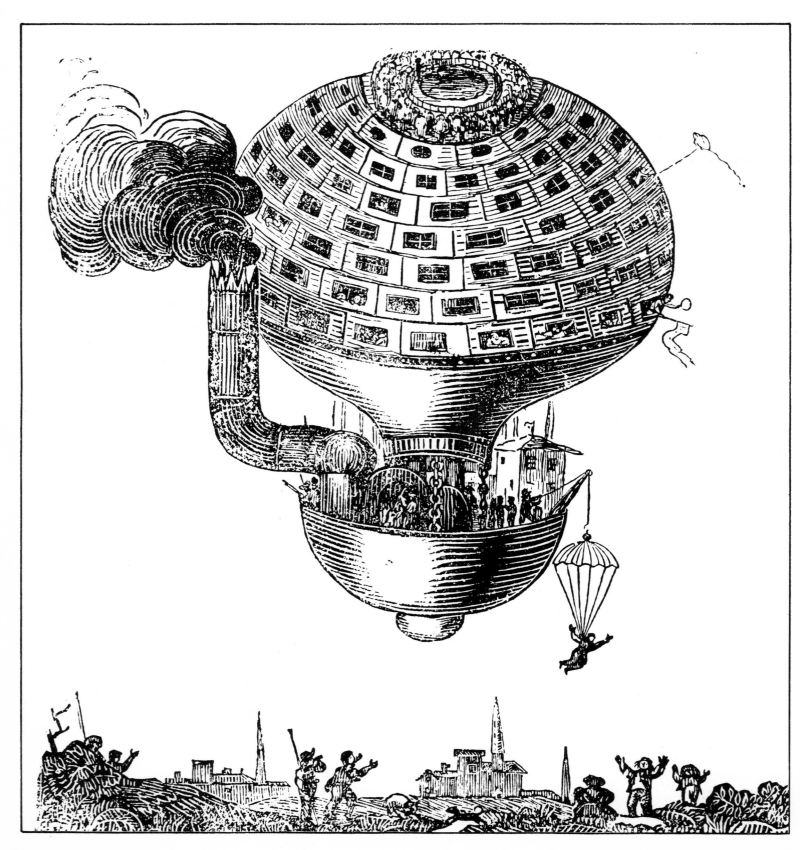

OH! the balloon, the great balloon
It left Vauxhall one Monday at noon,
And every one said we should hear of it soon
With news from Aleppo or Scanderoon.
But very soon after, folks changed their tune:
"The netting had burst—the silk—the shalloon:-
It had met with a trade-wind—a deuced monsoon—
It was blown out to sea—it was blown to the moon—
They ought to have put off their journey till June;
Sure none but a donkey, a goose, or baboon
Would go up, in November, in any balloon!"
Then they talk'd about Green—"Oh! where's Mister Green?
And where's Mr. Hollond who hired the machine?
And where is Monk Mason, the man that has been
Up so often before—twelve times or thirteen—
And who writes such nice letters describing the scene?
And where's the cold fowl, and the ham, and poteen?
The press'd beef, with the fat cut off—nothing but lean?
And the portable soup in the patent tureen?
Have they got to Grand Cairo or reached Aberdeen?
Or Jerusalem—Hamburgh—or Ballyporeen?
No! they have not been seen! Oh! they haven't been seen!

Stay! here's Mister Gye—Mr. Frederick Gye—
"At Paris," says he, "I've been up very high,
A couple of hundred of toises, or nigh,
A cockstride the Tuileries' pantiles, to spy
With Dollond's best telescope stuck at my eye,
And my umbrella under my arm like Paul Pry,
But I could see nothing at all but the sky:
So I thought with myself 'twas of no use to try
Any longer; and, feeling remarkably dry
From sitting all day stuck up there, like a Guy,
I came down again, and—you see—here am I!"

But here's Mr. Hughes!—What says young Mr. Hughes?—
"Why, I'm sorry to say we've not got any news
Since the letter they threw down in one of their shoes,
Which gave the Mayor's nose such a deuce of a bruise,
As he popp'd up his eye-glass to look at their cruise
Over Dover; and which the folks flocked to peruse
At Squier's bazaar, the same evening, in crews—
Politicians, news-mongers, town-council, and blues,
Turks, Heretics, Infidels, Jumpers, and Jews,
Scorning Bachelor's papers, and Warren's reviews:
But the wind was then blowing towards Helvoetsluys,
And my father and I are in terrible stews,
For so large a balloon is a sad thing to lose!"—

Here's news come at last;—Here's news come at last!—
A vessel's come in, which has sail'd very fast;
And a gentleman serving before the mast,—
Mister Nokes,—has declared "the party has past
Safe across to the Hague, where their grapnel they cast
As a fat burgomaster was staring aghast
To see such a monster come borne on the blast,
And it caught in his waistband, and there it stuck fast!"—
O fie! Mister Nokes,—for shame, Mr. Nokes!
To be poking your fun at us plain-dealing folks—
Sir, this isn't a time to be cracking your jokes,
And such jesting your malice but scurvily cloaks;
Such a trumpery tale every one of us smokes,
And we know very well your whole story's a hoax!—

"Oh! what shall we do?—Oh! where will it end?—
Can nobody go?—Can nobody send
To Calais—or Bergen-op-zoom—or Ostend?
Can't you go there yourself?—Can't you write to a friend,
For news upon which we may safely depend?"—

Huzza! huzza! one and eight-pence to pay
For a letter from Hamborough, just come to say
They descended at Weilburg, about break of day;
And they've lent them the palace there, during their stay,
And the town is becoming uncommonly gay,
And they're feasting the party, and soaking their clay
With Johannisberg, Rudesheim, Moselle, and Tokay!
And the Landgraves, and Margraves,
And Counts beg and pray
That they won't think, as yet, about going away;
Notwithstanding, they don't mean to make much delay,
But pack up the balloon in a waggon, or dray,
And pop themselves into a German "po-shay,"
And get on to Paris by Lisle and Tournay;
Where they boldly declare, any wager they'll lay
If the gas people there do not ask them to pay
Such a sum as must force them at once to say "Nay,"
They'll inflate the balloon in the Champs-Elysees,
And be back again here the beginning of May.—

Dear me! what a treat for a juvenile fete!
What thousands will flock their arrival to greet!
There'll be hardly a soul to be seen in the street,
For at Vauxhall the whole population will meet,
And you'll scarcely get standing-room, much less a seat,
For this all preceding attraction must beat:

Since, there they'll unfold, what we want to be told,
How they cough'd—how they sneez'd,—
How they shiver'd with cold,—
How they tippled the "cordial" as racy and old
As Hodges, or Deady, or Smith ever sold,
And how they all then felt remarkably bold:
How they thought the boil'd beef worth
Its own weight in gold,
And how Mister Green was beginning to scold
Because Mister Mason would try to lay hold
Of the moon, and had very near overboard roll'd!

And there they'll be seen—they'll be all to be seen!
The great-coats, the coffee-pot, mugs, and tureen!
With the tight rope, and fire works, and dancing between,
If the weather should only prove fair and serene,
And there, on a beautiful transparent screen,
In the middle you'll see a large picture of Green,
Mr. Hollond on one side, who hired the machine,
Mr. Mason on t'other, describing the scene;
And Fame, on one leg, in the air, like a queen,
With three wreaths and a trumpet, will over them lean;
While Envy, in serpents and black bombazine,
Looks on from below with an aire of chagrin!

Then they'll play up a tune in the Royal Saloon,
And the people will dance by the light of the moon,
And keep up the ball till the next day at noon;
And the peer and the peasant, the lord and the loon,
The haughty grandee, and the low picaroon,
The six-foot life-guardsman, and little gossoon,
Will all join in three cheers for the "Monstre" Balloon.

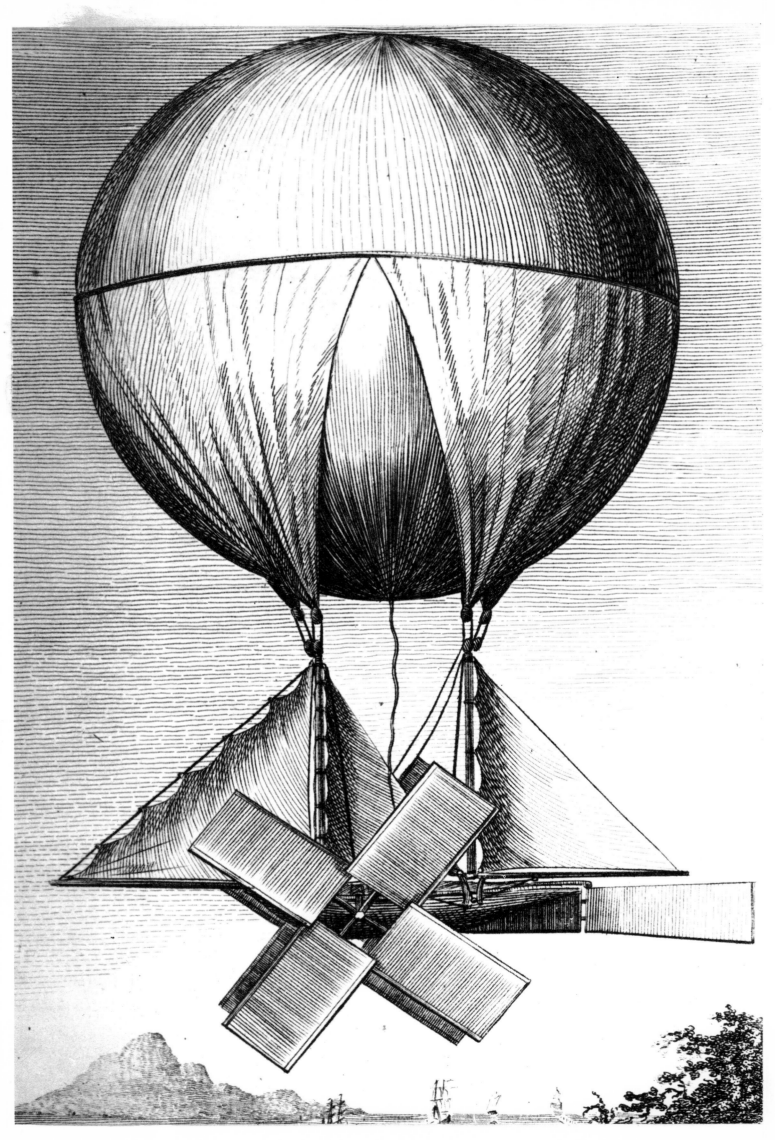

The success of simple balloons not only inspired the aeronauts to try for bigger and better things, but also caused a number of them to come up with the most extraordinary schemes. The balloon (above) complete with sails, rigging, cat-walk around the circumference and cannon was a British invention of the late 1800's which not surprisingly never got beyond the drawing board! The "Aeronautic Chariot" (opposite), however, was actually built and exhibited at Ranelagh near Dublin in August 1784. It was designed by a certain Richard Crosbie and an observer writing in a contemporary journal called it "one of the most remarkable efforts of human genius that has signalised itself in any country." The balloon from which the chariot was suspended was forty feet in diameter, while the boat section was made up of a light wood frame covered with linen. The windmill vanes on either side of the machine were to be turned "with such velocity . . . that they permit the sails to collect sufficient power to carry it ahead." For all this ingenuity, the 'Dream Machine' never flew successfully.

Entered at Stationers' Hall. | Pirates will be Prosecuted.

THE GREAT AERIAL NAVIGATOR, OR ATMOSPHERIC MACHINE!

Under the superintendence of the "Aerial Conveyance Company," for the conveying of Passengers, Troops, and Government Despatches to India and China, in the short space of Five Days, by means of a new and improved system of "AERIAL NAVIGATION" Adapted also to proceed on Water or Land, and can be used as a most destructive instrument of War; likewise for scientific and astronomical purposes: altogether forming in the wonderful adaptation of its various complicated parts, its mechanical combinations and mighty developement of power, one of the most extraordinary inventions of modern times.

Description.

This gigantic production of the genius of man, will assuredly become the greatest of all mechanical wonders, when its mighty powers for good and for evil are hereafter developed.

Aerial locomotion, on the old balloon principle has had its allotted time for exciting the wonder and admiration of the curious; but like stage coaches, balloons will soon be numbered among the things that were, as Atmospheric Machines of the above description are gradually adopted; in reality, annihilating both time and space, and by a more rapid intercommunication destroy the prejudices of nationality, and thus conduce to moral happiness.

No 1. Is the main body, or chief support of the whole apparatus; the only part which at all resembles the balloon principle. It is in the form of a heart, composed of 26,000 yds of finely woved and prepared silk, doubled throughout, somewhat in the form of a small balloon, enclosed within a larger one. It is to contain 160,000 feet of a newly discovered gas, formed by a secret chemical combination, considerably lighter than Coal Gas; while a fresh supply can always be kept up for the purpose of inflation, and thus obviate one of the greatest difficulties attendant upon the old system, both as regards power and security.

Around the internal part of the exterior covering is placed a *framework*, connected with another of smaller dimensions, but separate about two feet, resting upon the outside of the interior part which encloses the gas, composed of the strongest and best tempered steel, with whalebone wicker work, having slides and curiously formed joints, so, that the whole machine can be drawn together, and closely packed up after it has descended, and the gas evaporated.

2. & 4. Are *Parachutes*, so placed that when the main body of the machine is inflated, and ascends into the required current of air; they assist the power of suspension, and contribute to a more steady balance of the whole; thus entirely preventing the violent occillations that oftentimes occurred with the old balloons, and caused a very unpleasant sensation to be felt by novices in ærial locomotion. They can also be made to open and shut by means of their connection with the internal framework, and thus, by forcing on an average about 500lbs. weight of air each upon the main body, they consequently assist the machine in descending.

3. A *Telegraph*, situated on a small dome in the centre, at the top. It is composed of the same material as the interior frame work, of which it forms a part; and it has cross pieces so arranged as to serve the purpose of steps, by means of which ascension to, and descension from the telegraph can be easily effected. When within fifty miles of any place during clear weather, at a low elevation, or from 100 to 200 miles at higher and proportionably well situated elevations, various signals can be made to others at a distance, in the space of a few minutes, which is effected by working the two upright arms, and altering their positions as occasion may require. By those means persons can state their business and whatever they wish concerning the despatches, goods, and passengers they are conveying.

5. Is a *valve*, for conveying off the steam, when generated too quickly; it is raised by means of a double line at the back, and when required to be lowered other lines are attached to the fore part for that purpose. The steam is generated by quick lime and other chemical processes united. The valve is entirely of a new construction, containing within the pipe, and situated about the middle, a curiously constructed cylinder, and the top entirely opens when the cover is drawn up.

6. Another pipe, connected with the engine and chemical furnace, in the lower part of the machine, for carrying off the smoke and superfluous particles.

7. and 8. Are revolving *Fan-wheels*, connected with the internal frame before mentioned, and moved by the engine below, which so act as to fan the air with great force, and thus propel the machine forward. There are two others on the opposite side, for the like purpose. The fans are made of strong canvas, and revolve on the spokes; and their power of acting upon the atmosphere is equal to any of the larger kind of windmills.

9. Is another *Fan* of much greater power, in the form of the tail of a bird, which opens and shuts together, and moves up and down in the same manner, worked by the engine

before stated, and is situated at the *Stern* of the machine.

10. Shows an *Observatory*, with a most beautiful and very powerful Telescope, on the same principle as Sir John Herschell's grand instrument at the Cape of Good Hope. The mode of ascent and descent is by an enclosed staircase very curiously constructed. Like the gentleman here observed to be looking through the Telescope all lovers of science can enjoy themselves with greater pleasure than can be experienced on the earth.

11. At the base of the Observatory is the form of an eagle, the wings of which also act like fans, moved by machinery. On its head is a weather-cock, and out of its mouth is issuing smoke, which comes through a pipe placed in the interior, from the same place as mentioned in No. 6. This part forms the *Stem*, or *forepart* of the machine.

12. This is the upper part of the *Carriage* suspended to the main body of the machine, the same as a Car is usually attached to a balloon. It is called the *Day Chamber*, for the convenience and comfort of passengers in the daytime, when they want to enjoy the pure air and fine weather. It can also be used as a *Promenade* being sufficiently spacious for moderate exercise. Its dimensions are 24 feet long, by twelve feet wide, and 10 feet in height. It has a waterproof India rubber roof fixed in a mahogany frame, with handsome curtains which can be drawn together if required; supported by four beautiful veneered pillars and surrounded by a strong ballustrade, erected breast high, the whole fixed together in the most secure manner.

In the floor is a well-staircase, by which passengers can descend to what is called the *"Night Chamber,"* which is compact, warm and perfectly secured from the weather. It has a door in the centre on one side, and windows at each end on both sides of the chamber. It is of the same length as the upper chamber, but six feet wider and eight feet higher. Situate therein, enclosed within a fire-proof screen, is an *engine*, small in dimensions, but mighty in power, which moves the whole framework secreted in the internal part above and below, with every joint and member of its complicated machinery kept in constant and harmonious motion. Its Fans, Paddles, Wheels, Arms, Wings, and Tail, all working together—thus manifesting the ability of *man* to make every element of nature subservient to his purpose. At each end there are two private rooms, for either sex, so that every convenience that is possible in so small a space is adopted. One is the "Ladies' Department," and the other the "Gentlemen's," each room having chairs for six persons, a table, sofa, and all the small etceteras. The doors and partitions are made to take out, when the whole can be formed into a barrack for soldiers.

13. Is a boat, made (like the chambers above) after the Chinese fashion. It has a space of 6 feet on the deck, with bulwarks 3 feet high all round. Underneath, is a spacious hold, 9 feet in depth, for merchandise, naval or military stores, &c. There is a proof magazine for gunpowder, places for shot and shell, with 22 patent swivel guns, half of that number being placed on each side. Across the breech of each gun, over the touch-holes, is placed a *metallic rod*, one end of which is attached to a *Galvanic Battery*, and each gun is so constructed, that when the battery is charged, in a second of time a rapid succession of awful explosions will follow from the mouth of each piece of ordnance—pouring down their destructive fire almost perpendicular upon those unfortunates whoever might be exposed to it. In proportion, as the gas is expelled from the balloon part, it becomes filled with atmospheric air, and when it has descended by the other processes adopted for that purpose, if over the sea, or any navigable river, the boat can be made to float like vessels in the water, when the once gigantic *silk dome* above can be compactly folded up and then there appears sailing along a sort of *steam house*, to the "astonishment of the natives." Or, when it descends on land, then, the paddles can be drawn up, and the wheels can be used instead; when, behold! it now appears transformed into a steam carriage. "This is truly the age of wonders."

14, 15, 16, 17, 18, 19, 20, 21. Are *Fans, or Paddles*, the arms of which are moved by the *engine* before mentioned. They are constructed of india rubber, of an oval form, and hollow between the two sides, which are drawn tight on whalebone frames, with three air funnels on the sides and end of each of them, all composed of the same material which catch the air and adds to the force of their motions. They act as Fans in the atmosphere, and as Paddles in the water. This concludes our description of the external part of this "Great Aerial Navigator," and, there is nothing remaining to state respecting its internal arrangements excepting that the force of the engine, machinery, and chemical action on the whole, is equal to 200 horse power; also, it is calculated, that with 50 adult passengers, and when loaded with the amount of goods and other things it is required to carry, with the actual weight of the whole combined, it will not fall far short of 130 tons.

Incredible as it may appear to those ignorant of physical science, there is actually a *subtile and invisible agent*, known only to practical chemists, but first combined by the *Inventor*; which will suspend in the air even 20 times the above weight if used in proportion. With such means adopted for causing *Suspension*, also *Propulsion*, and *Repulsion*, by rising or falling into the required curent of air; and the principles of this machine brought into proper action, the public shall in a few months witness the glorious reality.

LETTER TO THE BOARD OF ORDNANCE.

London, Feb. 2[illegible] 1843.

MOST NOBLE LORDS, AND HONORABLE SIRS,

As it is your especial duty to superintend the offensive and defensive operations of Her Majesty's land forces; and as all inventions for acquiring superiority in the art of war, must become, when proved to be practicable, a subject of the greatest importance, especially to England; therefore, be it known unto you, that I have completed after many years study, that, which I flatter myself, you will pronouuce to be, one of the most extraordinary inventions of modern times, an Engraving of which, with a description, I here beg leave to lay before you.

A company of scientific gentlemen, the most experienced in the art of locomotion, has been formed for carrying into effect, that, which will ere long *prove a reality*, exhalt "fallen man," and elevate the whole human race in the scale of society. The unavoidable evils that will result by this invention clashing with other interests will only be of short duration, and will be compensated for, (nationally speaking) by the immense advantages that will accrue to England as the first of maritime countries, and the most universal of empires. That such will be the ultimate result, you will acknowledge when you have seriously read the above *description*. I remain, yours respectfully,

The Inventor.

TO HER MAJESTY'S MINISTERS.

London, Feb. 22nd. 1843.

MY LORDS AND GENTLEMEN,

Placed at the head of a great nation, I call on you to avail yourselves of my *invention*, which I will prove to you, if adopted, all the nations of the earth combined can never stand against our power. But, my Lords, I do not mention that fact, with the view of making my country the tyrant of the world, but for the more noble purpose of causing her to be the arbiter of every good. With that view I penned my former letters and my late one to the *"Board of Ordnance."* I am about to apply to Parliament for a "Bill" or "Act of Incorporation," in order that I might legalise a company of gentlemen associated with me, for the purpose of conveying passengers, goods, despatches, &c. by means of my *"Aerial Navigator,"* either through the air, on water or land. Hoping that I may depend on your support, I will conclude by laying before you the accompanying *Description*, of an invention which I justly feel proud of, conscious, that if rightly used, it will redound to the honour and glory of my native country, and the welfare of the whole civilised world.

I remain,
My Lords and Gentlemen,
Your Obedient Servant,
The Inventor.

VICKERS, Publisher, 28, Holywell Street, Strand; and supplied by W. Brittain, 11, Paternoster Row; Allen, Warwick Lane; Cleave, Shoe Lane; Purkess, Wardour Street; Clements, Pulteney Street; and if ordered, by all other Booksellers in Town or Country.
Letters (post-paid) attended to by K. HANCOCK, at J. Cook's, Printer, 1, Corner of Sadler's Buildings, Fann Street, Goswell Street

One of the largest of all the 'Monster' balloons that actually flew was the "Geant" which had a passenger carrying car the size of a two storey house! Over half a million people turned out to witness the two ascents of this giant in October 1863. It had been built by Eugene Godard for the French aeronaut-photographer Nader (Felix Tournachon, 1820-1910) who also founded a society for the promotion of heavier-than-air flying craft. The balloon held 210,000 cubic feet of gas and could carry a dozen passengers. The first flight, however, was short-lived, but the second covered over 400 miles before ending in one of the most publicised accidents in ballooning history. As the giant passed over Hanover, the pilot suddenly mistook a cloud bank for the sea and brought the balloon down to ground level. Immediately the basket began catching on trees and the passengers were dragged helplessly along for miles demolishing everything in their path. Amazingly, although some of the passengers were badly injured, none were actually killed. From the vast number of pictures and descriptions of the drama which exist, here (above) is one depicting the end of the ascent which has not previously been reproduced.

From a 'monster balloon' that flew we turn to perhaps the most extra-ordinary one which did not! (opposite) "The Great Aerial Navigator or Atmospheric Machine" was the brain child of the 'Aerial Conveyance Company' of London and planned to "Carry passengers, troops and Government Despatches to India and China in the short space of five days". The balloon was also claimed to be a "most destructive instrument of war" by the inventor who addressed a communique to Parliament in February 1843 urging the Government to adopt and finance his scheme. Not surprisingly, absolutely nothing happened.

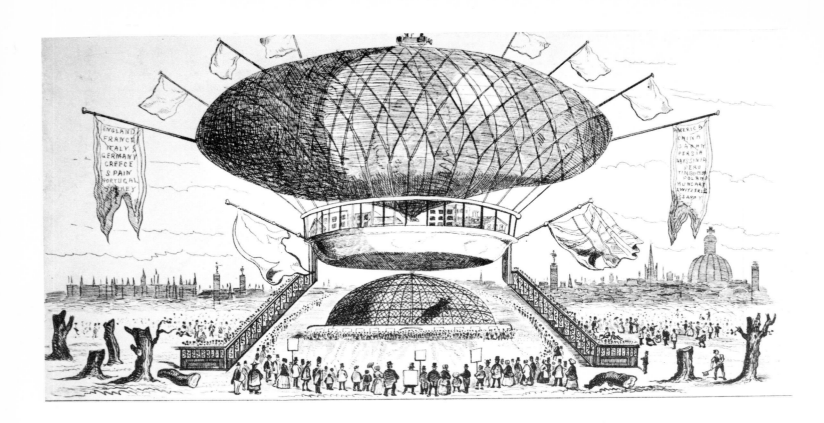

Another giant balloon which its inventor claimed could link the world's major cities in a matter of days was the subject of this amusing caricature (above) published in 1965. Apart from housing its passengers in actual buildings, the balloon was to have its own railway, systems of defence and the capacity to go round the world without stopping!

The poster is typical of those which appeared during the Eighteenth Century and is interesting at this point because of the size of the balloon it announces.

The Busted Balloon

George Cruikshank

*The great caricaturist and writer,
George Cruikshank (1792—1878)
could not resist a dig at the exploits of
the balloonists and here has some fun
in verse and illustration at the expense
of the balloonist Charles Green.*

Oh help! Oh help! Will no one come,
Our downward course to stay,
I will not, if I get safe home,
Come here another day!

To get to Paris over land,
Myself to this I trusted,
But when above the Goodwin sand,
Oh dear its gone and *busted!*

The Balloon-Hoax

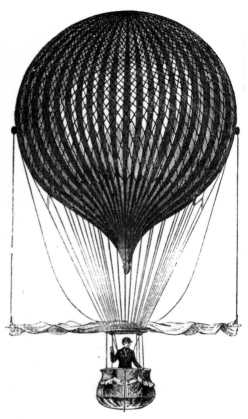

EDGAR ALLAN POE

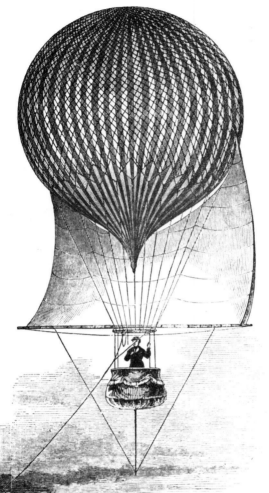

There is no more extraordinary story in Ballooning History than "The Balloon Hoax" by Edgar Allen Poe (1809—1849). It first appeared as an "extra" in the April 3rd 1844 issue of the "New York Sun" and created an immediate sensation. Presented in such a manner as to appear to be a true report, it was widely accepted as fact and led to much speculation that a regular balloon service backwards and forwards across the Atlantic was now feasible. In fact the story was pure invention on Poe's behalf and indeed the Atlantic remains uncrossed by balloon to this day despite several noble attempts.

Astounding News by Express, *via* Norfolk!—The Atlantic crossed in Three Days! Signal Triumph of Mr. Monck Mason's Flying Machine!—Arrival at Sullivan's Island, near Charleston, S.C., of Mr. Mason, Mr. Robert Hollond, Mr. Henson, Mr. Harrison Ainsworth, and four others, in the Steering Balloon, "Victoria," after a passage of Seventy-five Hours from Land to Land! Full Particulars of the Voyage!

The great problem is at length solved! The air, as well as the earth and the ocean, has been subdued by science, and will become a common and convenient highway for mankind. *The Atlantic has been actually crossed in a Balloon!* and this too without difficulty—without any great apparent danger—with thorough control of the machine—and in the inconceivably brief period of seventy-five hours from shore to shore! By the energy of an agent at Charleston, S.C., we are enabled to be the first to furnish the public with a detailed account of this most extraordinary voyage, which was performed between Saturday, the 6th instant, at 11 A.M., and 2 P.M., on Tuesday the 9th instant by Sir Everard Bringhurst; Mr. Osborne, a nephew of Lord Bentinck's; Mr. Monck Mason and Mr. Robert Hollond, the well-known aeronauts; Mr. Harrison Ainsworth, author of "Jack Sheppard," etc.; and Mr. Henson, the projector of the late unsuccessful flying-machine, with two seamen from Woolwich; in all, eight persons. The particulars furnished below may be relied on as authentic and accurate in every respect, as, with a slight exception, they are copied *verbatim* from the joint diaries of Mr. Monck Mason and Mr. Harrison Ainsworth, to whose politeness our agent is also indebted for much verbal information respecting the balloon itself, its construction, and other matters of interest. The only alteration in the MS. received, has been made for the purpose of throwing the hurried account of our agent, Mr. Forsyth, into a connected and intelligible form.

THE BALLOON

Two very decided failures of late—those of Mr. Henson and Sir George Cayley—had much weakened the public interest in the subject of aerial navigation. Mr. Henson's scheme (which at first was considered very feasible even by men of science) was founded upon the principle of an inclined plane, started from an eminence by an extrinsic force, applied and continued by the revolution of impinging vanes, in form and number resembling the vanes of a windmill. But, in all the experiments made with models at the Adelaide Gallery, it was found that the operation of these fans not only did not propel the machine, but actually impeded its flight. The only propelling force it ever exhibited was the mere *impetus* acquired from the descent of the inclined plane; and this *impetus* carried the machine farther when the vanes were at rest than when they were in motion, a fact which sufficiently demonstrates their inutility; and in the absence of the propelling, which was also the *sustaining* power, the whole fabric would necessarily descend. This consideration led Sir George Cayley to think only of adapting a propeller to some machine having of itself an independent power of support—in a word, to a balloon; the idea, however, being novel, or original, with Sir George, only so far as regards the mode of its application to practice. He exhibited a model of his invention at the Polytechnic Institution. The propelling principle or power was here also applied to interrupted surfaces or vanes put in revolution. These vanes were four in number, but were found entirely ineffectual in moving the balloon, or in aiding its ascending power. The whole project was thus a complete failure.

It was at this juncture that Mr. Monck Mason (whose voyage from Dover to Weilburg in the balloon, "Nassau," occasioned so much excitement in 1837) conceived the idea of employing the principle of the Archimedean screw for the purpose of propulsion through the air—rightly attributing the failure of Mr. Henson's scheme, and of Sir George Cayley's, to

the interruption of surface in the independent vanes. He made the first public experiment at Willis's Rooms, but afterwards removed his model to the Adelaide Gallery.

Like Sir George Cayley's balloon, his own was an ellipsoid. Its length was thirteen feet six inches—height, six feet eight inches. It contained about three hundred and twenty cubic feet of gas, which, if pure hydrogen, would support twenty-one pounds upon its first inflation, before the gas has time to deteriorate or escape. The weight of the whole machine and apparatus was seventeen pounds—leaving about four pounds to spare. Beneath the centre of the balloon, was a frame of light wood about nine feet long, and rigged on to the balloon itself with a network in the customary manner. From this framework was suspended a wicker basket or car.

The screw consists of an axis of hollow brass tube, eighteen inches in length, through which, upon a semi-spiral inclined at fifteen degrees, pass a series of a steel wire radii, two feet long, and thus projecting a foot on either side. These radii are connected at the outer extremities by two bands of flattened wire—the whole in this manner forming the framework of the screw, which is completed by a covering of oiled silk cut into gores, and tightened so as to present a tolerably uniform surface. At each end of its axis this screw is supported by pillars of hollow brass tube descending from the hoop. In the lower ends of these tubes are holes in which the pivots of the axis revolve. From the end of the axis which is next the car, proceeds a shaft of steel, connecting the screw with the pinion of a piece of spring machinery fixed in

the car. By the operation of this spring, the screw is made to revolve with great rapidity, communicating a progressive motion to the whole. By means of the rudder, the machine was readily turned in any direction. The spring was of great power compared with its dimensions, being capable of raising forty-five pounds upon a barrel of four inches diameter after the first turn, and gradually increasing as it was wound up. It weighed altogether eight pounds six ounces. The rudder was a light frame of cane covered with silk, shaped somewhat like a battle-door, and was about three feet long, and at the widest one foot. Its weight was about two ounces. It could be turned *flat*, and directed upwards or downwards, as well as to the right or left; and thus enabled the aeronaut to transfer the resistance of the air, which in an inclined position it must generate in its passage, to any side upon which he might desire to act, thus determining the balloon in the opposite direction.

This model (which, through want of time, we have necessarily described in an imperfect manner) was put in action at the Adelaide Gallery, where it accomplished a velocity of five miles per hour; although, strange to say, it excited very little interest in comparison with the previous complex machine of Mr. Henson—so resolute is the world to despise anything which carries with it an air of simplicity. To accomplish the great desideratum of aerial navigation, it was very generally supposed that some exceedingly complicated application must be made of some unusually profound principle in dynamics.

So well satisfied, however, was Mr. Mason of the ultimate success of his invention, that he determined to construct immediately, if possible, a balloon of sufficient capacity to test the question by a voyage of some extent—the original design being to cross the British Channel as before in the Nassau balloon. To carry out his views, he solicited and obtained the patronage of Sir Everard Bringhurst and Mr. Osborne, two gentlemen well known for scientific acquirement, and especially for the interest they have exhibited in the progress of aerostation. The project, at the desire of Mr. Osborne, was kept a profound secret from the public—the only persons entrusted with the design being those actually engaged in the

construction of the machine, which was built (under the superintendence of Mr. Mason, Mr. Hollond, Sir Everard Bringhurst, and Mr. Osborne) at the seat of the latter gentleman near Pen-struthal, in Wales. Mr. Henson, accompanied by his friend Mr. Ainsworth, was admitted to a private view of the balloon on Saturday last—when the two gentlemen made final arrangements to be included in the adventure. We are not informed for what reason the two seamen were also included in the party—but, in the course of a day or two, we shall put our readers in possession of the minutest particulars respecting this extraordinary voyage.

The balloon is composed of silk, varnished with the liquid gum caoutchouc. It is of vast dimensions, containing more than 40,000 cubic feet of gas; but as coal-gas was employed in place of the more expensive and inconvenient hydrogen, the supporting power of the machine when fully inflated, and immediately after inflation, is not more than about 2500 pounds. The coal-gas is not only much less costly, but is easily procured and managed.

For its introduction into common use for purposes of aerostation we are indebted to Mr. Charles Green. Up to his discovery, the process of inflation was not only exceedingly expensive, but uncertain. Two, and even three days, have frequently been wasted in futile attempts to procure a sufficiency of hydrogen to fill a balloon, from which it had great tendency to escape, owing to its extreme subtlety,

and its affinity for the surrounding atmosphere. In a balloon sufficiently perfect to retain its contents of coal-gas unaltered in quality or amount for six months, an equal quantity of hydrogen could not be maintained in equal purity for six weeks.

The supporting power being estimated at 2500 pounds, and the united weights of the party amounting only to about 1200, there was left a surplus of 1300, of which again 1200 was exhausted by ballast, arranged in bags of different sizes, with their respective weights marked upon them; by cordage, barometers, telescopes, barrels containing provision for a fortnight, water-casks, cloaks, carpet-bags, and various other indispensable matters, including a coffee-warmer, contrived for warming coffee by means of slack-lime, so as to dispense altogether with fire, if it should be judged prudent to do so. All these articles, with the exception of the ballast and a few trifles, were suspended from the hoop overhead. The car is much smaller and lighter in proportion than the one appended to the model. It is formed of a light wicker, and is wonderfully strong for so frail-looking a machine. Its rim is about four feet deep. The rudder is also very much larger in proportion than that of the model; and the screw is considerably smaller. The balloon is furnished besides with a grapnel and a guide-rope; which latter is of the most indispensable importance. A few words in explanation will here be necessary for such of our readers as

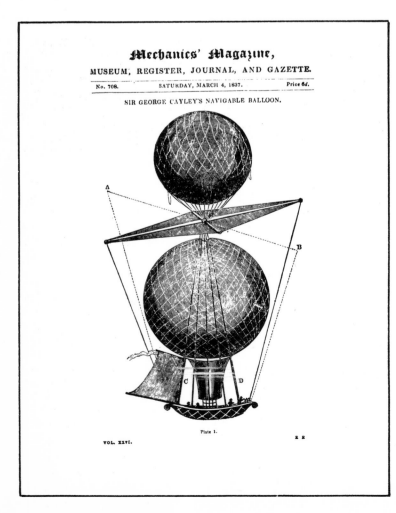

The idea of crossing the Atlantic obsessed balloonists in both Europe and America, but perhaps the inventor to have come closest to achieving this object was the Englishman, Sir George Cayley (1773-1857), widely accepted as the inventor of the aeroplane and one of the most important figures in the history of aviation. Apart from his later contribution in the design of the aeroplane, Sir George (left) had proposed in 1837 a navigeable balloon which could travel long distances and might well have had the Atlantic in its scope if the inventor had not left it to follow other plans.

In America, the idea of crossing the Atlantic so caught the imagination of the "New York Daily Graphic" that it agreed to finance an attempt at the crossing by the country's leading balloonist, John Wise, in 1873. While under construction, Wise's balloon was put on show in New York (right), but when it came to the actual attempt the craft only managed 41 miles before ditching.

Sea crossings have continued to present problems to balloonists, and even the English Channel has taken its toll as the picture above of a rescue in 1882 clearly shows. In this instance the two balloonists were beaten into the waves by high winds and fortuitously picked up by a passing mail-steamer.

are not conversant with the details of aerostation.

As soon as the balloon quits the earth it is subjected to the influence of many circumstances tending to create a difference in its weight, augmenting or diminishing its ascending power. For example, there may be a deposition of dew upon the silk to the extent even of several hundred pounds; ballast has then to be thrown out, or the machine may descend. This ballast being discarded, and a clear sunshine evaporating the dew, and at the same time expanding the gas in the silk, the whole will again rapidly ascend. To check this ascent, the only resource is (or rather *was*, until Mr. Green's invention of the guide-rope) the permission of the escape of gas from the valve; but, in the loss of gas, is a proportionate general loss of ascending power; so that in a comparatively brief period the best constructed balloon must necessarily exhaust all its resources and come to the earth. This was the great obstacle to voyages of length.

The guide-rope remedies the difficulty in the simplest manner conceivable. It is merely a very long rope which is suffered to trail from the car, and the effect of which is to prevent the balloon from changing its level in any material degree. If, for example, there should be a deposition of moisture upon the silk, and the machine begins to descend in consequence, there will be no necessity for discharging ballast to remedy the increase of weight, for it is remedied or counteracted in an exactly just proportion by the deposit on the ground of just so much of the end of the rope as is necessary. If, on the other hand, any circumstances should cause undue levity, and consequent ascent, this levity is immediately counteracted by the additional weight of rope upraised from the earth. Thus, the balloon can

neither ascend nor descend, except within very narrow limits, and its resources, either in gas or ballast, remain comparatively unimpaired. When passing over an expanse of water it becomes necessary to employ small kegs of copper or wood filled with liquid ballast of a lighter nature than water. These float, and serve all the purposes of a mere rope on land. Another most important office of the guide-rope is to point out the *direction* of the balloon. The rope *drags*, either on land or sea, while the balloon is free; the latter, consequently, is always in advance when any progress whatever is made; a comparison, therefore, by means of the compass of the relative positions of the two objects will always indicate the *course*. In the same way, the angle formed by the rope with the vertical axis of the machine indicates the *velocity*. When there is *no* angle—in other words, when the rope hangs perpendicularly, the whole apparatus is stationary; but the larger the angle, that is to say, the farther the balloon precedes the end of the rope, the greater the velocity; and the converse.

As the original design was to cross the British Channel, and alight as near Paris as possible, the voyagers had taken the precaution to prepare themselves with passports directed to all parts of the Continent, specifying the nature of the expedition, as in the case of the Nassau voyage, and entitling the adventurers to exemption from the usual formalities of office. Unexpected events, however, rendered these passports superfluous.

The inflation was commenced very quietly at day-break, on Saturday morning, the 6th instant, in the Court-yard of Weal-Vor House, Mr. Osborne's seat, about a mile from Penstruthal, in North Wales; and at 7 minutes past 11, everything being ready for departure, the balloon was set free, rising gently

but steadily in a direction nearly south, no use being made for the first half-hour of either the screw or the rudder. We proceed now with the journal as transcribed by Mr. Forsyth from the joint MSS. of Mr. Monck Mason and Mr. Ainsworth. The body of the journal, as given, is in the handwriting of Mr. Mason, and a P.S. is appended each day by Mr. Ainsworth, who has in preparation, and will shortly give the public, a more minute and, no doubt, a thrillingly interesting account of the voyage.

THE JOURNAL

Saturday, April the 6th.—Every preparation likely to embarrass us having been made over night, we commenced the inflation this morning at day-break; but owing to a thick fog, which encumbered the folds of the silk and rendered it unmanageable, we did not get through before nearly 11 o'clock. Cut loose, then, in high spirits, and rose gently but steadily, with a light breeze at north, which bore us in the direction of the British Channel. Found the ascending force greater than we had expected; and as we arose higher and so got clear of the cliffs, and more in the sun's rays, our ascent became very rapid. I did not wish, however, to lose gas at so early a period of the adventure, and so concluded to ascend for the present. We soon ran out our guide-rope; but even when we had raised it clear of the earth, we still went up very rapidly. The balloon was unusually steady, and looked beautiful. In about ten minutes after starting the barometer indicated an altitude of 15,000 feet. The weather was remarkably fine, and the view of the subjacent country—a most romantic one when seen from any point— was now especially sublime. The numerous deep gorges presented the appearance of lakes, on account of the dense vapours with which they were filled,

The most adventurous project for crossing the Atlantic surely came from the Americans, and the great pioneer T. S. C. Lowe, who built an aerostat for this purpose at Hoboken, New Jersey in 1859. The balloon, (left) "The Great Western" was 130 feet in diameter, weighted 2½ tons, and could carry six passengers. Unfortunately, lack of funds, a string of minor disasters and attacks in the press ("this great balloon humbug") brought the project to nought.

and the pinnacles and crags to the south-east, piled in inextricable confusion, resembled nothing so much as the giant cities of eastern fable. We were rapidly approaching the mountains in the south, but our elevation was more than sufficient to enable us to pass them in safety. In a few minutes we soared over them in fine style; and Mr. Ainsworth, with the seamen, were surprised at their apparent want of altitude when viewed from the car, the tendency of great elevation in a balloon being to reduce inequalities of the surface below to nearly a dead level. At half-past eleven, still proceeding nearly south, we obtained our first view of the Bristol Channel; and, in fifteen minutes afterwards, the line of breakers on the coast appeared immediately beneath us, and we were fairly out at sea. We now resolved to let off enough gas to bring our guide-rope, with the buoys affixed, into the water. This was immediately done, and we commenced a gradual descent. In about twenty minutes our first buoy dipped, and at the touch of the second soon afterwards we remained stationary as to elevation. We were all now anxious to test the efficiency of the rudder and screw, and we put them both into requisition forthwith, for the purpose of altering our direction more to the eastward, and in a line for Paris. By means of the rudder we instantly effected the necessary change of direction, and our course was brought nearly at right angles to that of the wind; when we set in motion the spring of the screw, and were rejoiced to find it propel us readily as desired. Upon this we gave nine hearty cheers, and dropped in the sea a bottle, enclosing a slip of parchment with a brief account of the principle of the invention. Hardly, however, had we done with our rejoicings, when an unforeseen accident occurred which discouraged us in no little degree. The steel rod connecting the spring with the propeller was suddenly jerked out of place at the car end (by a swaying of the car through some movement of one of the two seamen we had taken up), and in an instant hung dangling out of reach from the pivot of the axis of the screw. While we were endeavouring to regain it, our attention being completely absorbed, we became involved in a strong current of wind from the east, which bore us with rapidly increasing force towards the Atlantic. We soon found ourselves driving out to sea at the rate of not less, certainly, than fifty or sixty miles an hour, so that we came up with Cape Clear, at some forty miles to our north, before we had secured the rod and had time to think what we were about. It was now that Mr. Ainsworth made an extraordinary, but, to my fancy, a by no means unreasonable or chimerical proposition, in which he was instantly seconded by Mr. Hollond—viz., that

we should take advantage of the strong gale which bore us on, and in place of beating back to Paris, make an attempt to reach the coast of North America. After slight reflection I gave a willing assent to this bold proposition, which (strange to say) met with objection from the two seamen only. As the stronger party, however, we overruled their fears, and kept resolutely upon our course. We steered due west; but as the trailing of the buoys materially impeded our progress, and we had the balloon abundantly at command, either for ascent or descent, we first threw out fifty pounds of ballast, and then wound up (by means of a windlass) so much of a rope as brought it quite clear of the sea. We perceived the effect of this manoeuvre immediately in a vastly increased rate of progress; and, as the gale freshened, we flew with a velocity nearly inconceivable—the guide-rope flying out behind the car like a streamer from a vessel. It is needless to say that a very short time sufficed us to lose sight of the coast. We passed over innumerable vessels of all kinds, a few of which were endeavouring to beat up, but the most of them lying to. We occasioned

the greatest excitement on board all—an excitement greatly relished by ourselves, and especially by our two men, who, now under the influence of a dram of Geneva, seemed resolved to give all scruple or fear to the wind. Many of the vessels fired signal guns; and in all we were saluted with loud cheers (which we heard with surprising distinctness) and the waving of caps and handkerchiefs. We kept on in this manner throughout the day with no material incident, and as the shades of night closed around us we made a rough estimate of the distance traversed. It could not have been less than five hundred miles, and was probably much more. The propeller was kept in constant operation, and no doubt aided our progress materially. As the sun went down, the gale freshened into an absolute hurricane, and the ocean beneath was clearly visible on account of its phosphorescence. The wind was from the east all night, and gave us the brightest omen of success. We suffered no little from cold, and the dampness of the atmosphere was most unpleasant; but the ample space in the car enabled us to lie down, and by means of cloaks and a few blankets, we did sufficiently well.

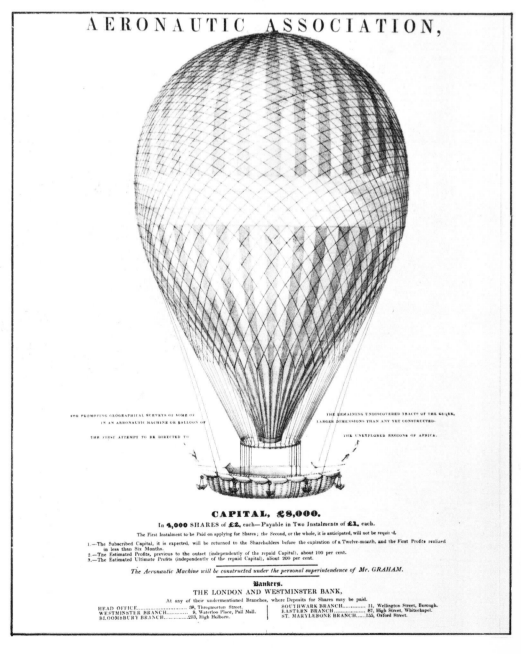

AERONAUTIC ASSOCIATION,

FOR PROMOTING GEOGRAPHICAL SURVEYS OF SOME OF

IN AN AERONAUTIC MACHINE OR BALLOON OF

THE FIRST ATTEMPT TO BE DIRECTED TO

THE REMAINING UNDISCOVERED TRACTS OF THE GLOBE,

LARGER DIMENSIONS THAN ANY YET CONSTRUCTED.

THE UNEXPLORED REGIONS OF AFRICA.

CAPITAL, £8,000.

In 4,000 SHARES of £2, each—Payable in Two Instalments of £1, each.

The First Instalment to be Paid on applying for Shares; the Second, or the whole, it is anticipated, will not be required.

1.—The Subscribed Capital, it is expected, will be returned to the Shareholders before the expiration of a Twelve-month, and the First Profits realized in less than Six Months.
2.—The Estimated Profits, previous to the outset (independently of the repaid Capital), about 100 per cent.
3.—The Estimated Ultimate Profits (independently of the repaid Capital), about 200 per cent.

The Aeronautic Machine will be constructed under the personal superintendence of Mr. GRAHAM.

Bankers.

THE LONDON AND WESTMINSTER BANK,

At any of their undermentioned Branches, where Deposits for Shares may be paid.

HEAD OFFICE..............................38, Threadneedle Street.	SOUTHWARK BRANCH...............3, Wellington Street, Borough.
WESTMINSTER BRANCH...........9, Waterloo Place, Pall Mall.	EASTERN BRANCH...................87, High Street, Whitechapel.
BLOOMSBURY BRANCH............213, High Holborn.	ST. MARYLEBONE BRANCH.......155, Oxford Street.

THE NEW AERIAL STEAM SHIP;
OR, THE BISHOPS' TRIP TO H——N.

The much talked of invention of an Aerial Steam Ship, different from all others hitherto conceived, has been realized, and will very shortly be brought into practice. It is now understood in the best informed circles of science, that the Bench of Bishops have expressly engaged this wonderful machine for an experimental trip to ALL'S BLUE; and have entered into engagements with Old Conkey, as Pilot; Peel as Helmsman, the Archbishop of Canterbury, Captain and Prime Director of course, and who (we state this also as a fact) was seen the other night on the top of the spire of St PETER'S, Cornhill, endeavouring to force off the GREAT GILDED KEY, but only partially succeeded, owing to the D——l in a high wind, though no doubt he will ultimately effect his object, without which indispensable instrument, 'tis said, the Right Reverend Fathers in Bob cannot enter into H———n.

N. B. We would call the attention of the numerous Emigration Companies to the above Machine, as admirably adapted for the emigration of the SURPLICE Population.

P.S. [By Mr. Ainsworth.] The last nine hours have been unquestionably the most exciting of my life. I can conceive nothing more sublimating than the strange peril and novelty of an adventure such as this. May God grant that we succeed! I ask not success for mere safety to my insignificant person, but for the sake of human knowledge, and for the vastness of the triumph. And yet the feat is only so evidently feasible that the sole wonder is why men have scrupled to attempt it before. One single gale such as now befriends us—let such a tempest whirl forward a balloon for four or five days (these gales often last longer), and the voyager will be easily borne in that period from coast to coast. In view of such a gale the broad Atlantic becomes a mere lake. I am more struck just now with the supreme silence which reigns in the sea beneath us, notwithstanding its agitation, than with any other phenomenon presenting itself. The waters give up no voice to the heavens. The immense flaming ocean writhes and is tortured uncomplainingly. The mountainous surges suggest the idea of innumerable dumb gigantic fiends struggling in impotent agony. In a night such as is this to me, a man *lives*—lives a whole century of ordinary life—nor would I forego this rapturous delight for that of a whole century of ordinary existence.

Sunday, the 7th. [Mr. Mason's MS.] This morning the gale, by 10, had subsided to an eight or nine knot breeze (for a vessel at sea), and bears us, perhaps, thirty miles per hour or more. It has veered, however, very considerably to the north; and now, at sundown, we are holding our course due west, principally by the screw and rudder, which answer their purposes to admiration. I regard the project as thoroughly successful, and the easy navigation of the air in any direction (not exactly in the teeth of a gale) as no longer problematical. We could not have made head against the strong wind of yesterday; but, by ascending, we might have got out of its influence if requisite. Against a pretty stiff breeze, I feel convinced we can make our way with the propeller. At noon to-day ascended to an elevation of nearly 25,000 feet by discharging ballast. Did this to search for a more direct current, but found none so favourable as the one we are now in. We have an abundance of gas to take us across this small pond even should the voyage last three weeks. I have not the slightest fear for the result. The difficulty has been strangely exaggerated and misapprehended. I can choose my current, and should I find *all* currents against me, I can make very tolerable headway with the propeller. We have had no incidents worth recording. The night promises fair.

P.S. [By Mr. Ainsworth.] I have little to record, except the fact (to me quite a surprising one) that, at an elevation equal to that of Cotopaxi, I experienced neither very intense cold, nor headache, not difficulty of breathing; neither, I find, did Mr. Mason, nor Mr. Hollond, nor Sir Everard. Mr. Osborne complained of constriction of the chest—but this soon wore off. We have flown at a great rate during the day, and we must be more than half way across the Atlantic. We have passed over some twenty or thirty vessels of various kinds, and all seem to be delightfully astonished. Crossing the ocean in a balloon is not so difficult a feat after all. *Omne ignotum pro magnifico. Mem.*—At 25,000 feet elevation the sky appears nearly black, and the stars are distinctly visible; while the sea does not seem convex (as one might suppose), but absolutely and most unequivocally *concave.* [1]

Monday, the 8th. [Mr. Mason's MS.] This morning we had again some little trouble with the rod of the propeller, which must be entirely remodelled for fear of serious accident—I mean the steel rod, not the vanes. The latter could not be improved. The wind has been blowing steadily and strongly from the north-east all day; and so far fortune seems bent upon favouring us. Just before day we were all somewhat alarmed at some odd noises and concussions in the balloon, accompanied with the apparent rapid subsidence of the whole machine. These phenomena were occasioned by the expansion of the gas, through increase of heat in the atmosphere, and the consequent disruption of the minute particles of ice with which the net-work had become encrusted during the night. Threw down several bottles to the vessels below. Saw one of them picked up by a large ship—seemingly one of the New York line packets. Endeavoured to make out her name, but could not be sure of it. Mr. Osborne's telescope made it out something like "Atalanta." It is now 12 at night, and we are still going nearly west at a rapid pace. The sea is peculiarly phosphorescent.

P.S. [By Mr. Ainsworth.] It is now 2 A.M., and nearly calm, as well as I can judge—but it is very difficult to determine this point, since we move *with* the air so completely. I have not slept since quitting Weal-Vor, but can stand it no longer, and must take a nap. We cannot be far from the American coast.

Tuesday, the 9th. [Mr. Ainsworth's MS.] 1 P.M. *We are in full view of the low coast of South Carolina.* The great problem is accomplished. We have crossed the Atlantic—fairly and *easily* crossed it in a balloon! God be praised! Who shall say that anything is impossible hereafter?

The Journal here ceases. Some particulars of the descent were communicated, however, by Mr. Ainsworth to Mr. Forsyth. It was nearly dead calm when the voyagers first came in view of the coast, which was immediately recognised by both the seamen, and by Mr. Osborne. The latter gentleman having acquaintances at Fort Moultrie, it was immediately resolved to descend in its vicinity. The balloon was brought over the beach (the tide being out and the sand hard, smooth, and admirably adapted for a descent), and the grapnel let go, which took firm hold at once. The inhabitants of the island and of the fort thronged out of course to see the balloon; but it was with the greatest difficulty that any one could be made to credit the actual voyage—*the crossing of the Atlantic.* The grapnel caught at 2 P.M. precisely; and thus the whole voyage was completed in seventy-five hours, or rather less, counting from shore to shore. No serious accident occurred. No real danger was at any time apprehended. The balloon was exhausted and secured without trouble; and when the MS. from which this narrative is compiled, was despatched from Charleston the party was still at Fort Moultrie. Their further intentions were not ascertained, but we can safely promise our readers some additional information either on Monday or in the course of the next day at furthest.

This is unquestionably the most stupendous, the most interesting, and the most important undertaking ever accomplished or even attempted by man. What manificent events may ensue it would be useless now to think of determining.

THE ÆRIAL SHIP

A Comic Ballad.
SUNG BY
Mr W. H. WILLIAMS.
with unbounded applause
AT THE
ROYAL COLOSSEUM,
The Birmingham & Bath Festivals &c.
POETRY BY
W. H. Freeman Esqre
THE MUSIC COMPOSED BY
ROBT EVANS.

Ent. Sta. Hall.   Price 2

LONDON. [1835]
Published by R. EVANS. 156. Strand. (near Somerset House)
Where may be had W. H. Williams's Celebrated Comic Songs.
"ALL ROUND MY HAT" "GOING OUT SHOOTING" "LADIES WHO'LL BUY" &c. &c. &c.

---

[1] Mr. Ainsworth has not attempted to account for this phenomenon, which, however, is quite susceptible of explanation. A line dropped from an elevation of 25,000 feet perpendicularly to the surface of the earth (or sea) would form the perpendicular of a right-angled triangle, of which the base would extend from the right angle to the horizon, and the hypothenuse from the horizon to the balloon. But the 25,000 feet of altitude is little or nothing in comparison with the extent of the prospect. In other words, the base and hypothenuse of the supposed triangle would be so long when compared with the perpendicular, that the two former may be regarded as nearly parallel. In this manner the horizon of the aeronaut would appear to be *on a level* with the car. But as the point immediately beneath him seems, and is, at a great distance below him, it seems, of course, also at a great distance below the horizon. Hence the impression of *concavity*; and this impression must remain until the elevation shall bear so great a proportion to the extent of prospect, that the apparent parallelism of the base and hypothenuse disappears—when the earth's real convexity must become apparent.

"In the Clouds"

or the Account of a Balloon Trip with Mr. Green   Henry Mayhew

G.P. Harding, F.S.A. *[illegible]* delt. et fect.

M.R CHARLES GREEN, AERONAUT.

Henry Mayhew (1812-1887) who chronicled the plight of London's poor and the terrors of the criminal underworld with such graphic detail, was certainly one of the 19th Century's greatest journalists. Like all men of print he was forever ready to take on any unusual assignment and none more so than a trip with the most famous balloonist of the age, Mr. Charles Green. His long out of print report on their flight is reprinted here.

I am naturally a coward—constitutionally and habitually timid—I do not hesitate to confess it. The literary temperament and sedentary pursuits are, I believe, seldom associated with physical courage. Fear, or the ideal presence of prospective injury, is necessarily an act of the imagination; and the sense of danger, therefore, closely connected with a sense of the beautiful and the aesthetic faculties in general. Your human bull-dogs are mostly deficient in mental refinement, and perhaps if there be any class of characters more fancyless than the rest of the world, they are those who are said to belong to the "fancy". My creed is that all imaginative men are cowards; and that I am one I have at least moral courage and honesty enough to acknowledge.

Then why go up in a balloon?

Yes, why? These are times when men's principles of action are sure to be canvassed; so, to prevent the imputation of any false motives, I will make a clean breast of it, and confess that it was merely "idle curiosity," as the world calls it that took me into the air.

I had seen the great metropolis under almost every aspect. I had dived into holes and corners hidden to the honest and well-to-do-portion of the cockney community. I had visited Jacob's Island (the plague spot) in the height of the cholera, when, to inhale the very air of the place was almost to breathe the breath of death. I had sought out the haunts of the beggars and thieves, and passed hours communing with them as to their histories, habits, natures

and impulses. I had seen the world of London below the surface, as it were, and I had a craving to contemplate it far above it—to behold the immense mass of vice and avarice and cunning, of noble aspirations and humble heroism, blended into one black spot; to take, as it were an angel's view of the huge city where, perhaps, there is more virtue and more iniquity, more wealth and more want huddled together in one vast heap than in any other part of the earth; to look down upon the strange, incongruous clump of palaces and workhouses, of factory chimneys and church steeples, of banks and prisons, of docks and hospitals, of parks and squares, of courts and alleys—to look down upon these as the birds in the air look down upon them, and see the whole dwindle into a heap of rubbish on the green sward, a human ant-hill, as it were; to hear the hubbub of the restless sea of life below, and hear it like an ocean in a shell, whispering to you of the incessant strugglings of chafings and distant tide—to swing in the air far above all the petty jealousies and heart burnings, and small ambitions and vain parades—and feel for once tranquil as a babe in a cot—that you were hardly on earth ; and to find, as you drank in the pure thin air above you, the blood dancing and tingling joyously through your veins, and your whole spirit becoming etherealised as Jacob-like, you mounted the aerial ladder, and beheld the world beneath you fade and fade from your sight like a mirage in the desert; to feel yourself really, as you had ideally in your dreams, floating through the endless realms of space, sailing among the stars free as "the lark at heaven's gate;" and to enjoy for a brief half-hour at least a foretaste of that elysian destiny which is the hope of all. To see, to think, and to feel thus was surely some little risk, and this it was that led me to peril my bones in the car of a balloon.

It is true that the aerial bulls and ponies of late had taken nearly all poetry from the skies, reducing the ancient myths to the mere stage trickeries of an ethereal Astley's; true that the depraved rage for excitement—that species of

This dramatic and evocative illustration of Charles Green's balloon landing at night on Purbright Common, Surrey appeared with Henry Mayhew's account of his voyage with the aeronaut. Green (1785-1870) was undoubtedly Britain's most popular balloonist

during the Nineteenth Century and attracted enormous, enthusiastic crowds wherever he appeared. The picture is taken from "The Illustrated London News" of September 18, 1852.

Two of the many posters which heralded the appearances of Charles Green. His ascents were considered the highlight of any popular festival or exhibition and promoters were never slow to include him in their plans.

mental dram drinking which ever demand some brutal stimulant—had given a most vulgar, prosaic character to a voyage which, when stripped of its peril, was perhaps one of the surest and most dignified delights that the mind was capable of enjoying; still, quickened with a love of my own art, and heedless of any silly imputations of rivalry with quadrupeds and mountebanks, I gladly availed myself of a seat in the car which Mr. Green had set aside for me.

At about a quarter to seven o'clock, six of us and the "veteran aeronaut" took our places in the large deep wicker buck-basket of a car attached to the Royal Nassau Balloon, while two gentlemen were seated immediately above our heads, with their backs resting against the netting and their legs stretched across the hoop to which the cords of the net-work are fastened, and from which depends the car. There were altogether nine of us—a complete set of human pins for the air to play at skittles with—and the majority, myself above the number, no sylphs in weight. Above us reeled the great gas-bag like a monster peg-top, and all around the car were groups of men holding to the sides of the basket, while the huge iron weights were handed out and replaced by large squabby bags of sand.

In the course of about ten minutes all the arrangements for starting were complete, the grapnel, looking like a bundle of large iron fishhooks, welded together, was hanging over the side of the car. The guide-rope, longer than St. Paul's is high, and done up in a canvas bag, with only the end hanging out, was dangling beside the grapnel, and we were raised some fifty feet in the air to try the ascensive power

of the machine that was to bear us through the clouds. Then, having been duly dragged down, the signal was at length given to fire the cannons, and Mr. Green loosening the only rope that bound us to the Gardens, we shot into the air—or rather the earth seemed to sink suddenly down, as if the spot of ground, with all the spectators on it, and on which we ourselves had been lately standing, had been constructed on the same principle as the Adelphi stage and admitted of being lowered at a moment's notice. The last thing that I remember to have seen distinctly was the flash of the guns and instantaneously there appeared a multitude of upturned faces in the Gardens below, the greater part with their mouths wide open, and a *cheveux de frise* of hands extended above them, all signalling farewell to us. Then, as we swept rapidly above the trees, I could see the roadway immediately outside the Gardens, stuck all over with rows of tiny people, looking like so many black pins on a cushion, and the hubbub of the voices below was like the sound of a distant school let loose.

And here began that peculiar panoramic effect which is the distinguishing feature of a view from a balloon, and which arises from the utter absence of all sense of motion in the machine itself. The earth appeared literally to consist of a long series of scenes, which were being continually drawn along under you, as if it were a diorama beheld flat upon the ground, and gave you almost the notion that the world was an endless landscape stretched upon rollers, which some invisible sprites were revolving for your special enjoyment.

THE NEW GRAND BALLOON,

Which is to ascend this day (September the 23d, 1836) from Vauxhall Gardens, with **Ten Persons**.

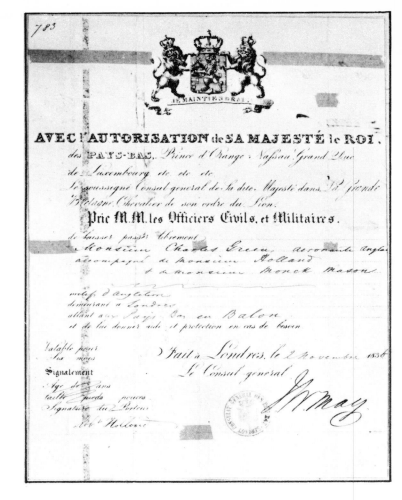

There have been few balloonists more important than Charles Green and fewer still whose influence extended further than his did in Britain across Europe and over the Atlantic to America. An enthusiastic balloonist from an early age, he made his first trip in 1821 and his last — his five hundredth—in 1870 when he was 85 years old! His two major contributions to aerostation were the introduction of coal gas for lifting balloons (in 1821) and the use of a trail-rope — although he is perhaps best remembered for his classic 480 mile balloon journey from the Vauxhall Gardens, London to the Duchy of Nassau in Germany in November 7-8, 1836. This adventure, sponsored by the M.P. Robert Hollond, was undertaken by Green with his friend, the writer Monck Mason, primarily to test the new trail-rope, but turned into a long-distance flight. The journey lasted for eighteen hours and the distance covered stood as a record until 1907. (For this trip the two men were actually issued with the first air passport which is reproduced here.) After the ascent, Green's balloon, which up until then had been known as the "Royal Vauxhall" was renamed "The Great Balloon of Nassau" and it was a constant attraction in the capitals of Europe as the posters on this page from France and Germany clearly show. Charles Green made a number of other important balloon trips including the first ascent to carry out scientific tests in September 1852 (opposite). The four men went up to an altitude of 19,200 feet and although the temperature sank to 25 degrees below freezing point none of them suffered any ill-effects. (Several later expeditions, however, were to suffer badly from frost-bite and loss of oxygen.) Charles Green eventually died quietly at home in his bed after a lifetime of unique aeronautical pioneering.

Then, as we struck towards the fields of Surrey, and I looked over the edge of the car in which I was standing, holding on tight to the thick rope descending from the hoop above, and with the rim of the wicker work reaching up to my breast, the sight was the most exquisite delight I ever experienced. The houses below looked like the tiny wooden things out of a child's box of toys, and the street like ruts. To peer straight down gave you an awful sense of the height to which the balloon had already risen, and yet there was no idea of danger, for the mind was too much occupied with the grandeur and novelty of the scene all around to feel the least alarm. As the balloon kept on ascending, the lines of buildings grew smaller and smaller, till in a few minutes the projections seemed very much like the prominences on the little coloured plaster models of countries. Then we could see the gas lights along the different lines of road start into light one after another all over the earth, and presently the ground seemed to be covered with little miniature illumination lamps, such as may be seen resting on the grass at the edge of gravel walks in suburban gardens of amusement. The river we could see winding far away, undulating, as it streamed along, like a man-of-war's pennant, and glittering here and there in the dusk like grey steel. All round the horizon were thick slate-covered clouds, edged with the orange of the departed sun; and with the tops of these we seemed to be on a level. So deep was the dusk in the distance, that it was difficult to tell where the earth ended and the sky began; and in trying to make out the objects afar off, it seemed to be as if you were looking through so much crape. The roads below were now like narrow light-brown ribbons, and the bridges across the Thames almost like planks; while the tiny black barges, as they floated up the river, appeared no bigger than insects. The large green fields had dwindled down to about the size of kettleholders, and the hedges were like strips of chenille.

When we were about a mile above the ground some of us threw pieces of paper into the grey air, and that, as we rose and left them below, fluttering about like butterflies as they fell. Then some of the more noisy of the crew struck a song; while I heard a dyspeptic gentleman immediately behind me, as I was kneeling down (for there was but one seat), and stretching my head over the side of the car, contemplating the world of wonder below, confess to feeling a little nervous, saying that he was a man of natural courage, but his body overcame it as he was subject to fits of indigestion and as a preventive to extreme nervousness had taken nothing but vegetables for dinner that day. And I must confess myself that, poised up high in the air, as we were, with but a few slender cords to support us, I could not help thinking of the awful havoc there would be if the twigs of the wicker car were to break and the bottom to give away.

On what sharp steeple thought I should I be spitted, and as I looked down the beauty of the scene once more took all sense of fear from my mind, for the earth now appeared concave with the height, and seemed like a huge black bowl—as if it were the sky of the nether regions. The lights of the village scattered over the scene, were like clusters of glow-worms, from the midst of which you could here and there distinguish the crimson speck of some railway lamp.

"There, I've thrown over a letter, directed to my house," said one of the passengers, "telling 'em we're safe up here"—and as I stretched over the car I saw the little white fluttering thing go zigzaging down the air, while we still mounted the sky.

Then some of the passengers, who had supplied themselves with an extraordinary stock of courage previous to starting, by means of sundry bottles of "sparkling champagne," which had the effect of making them more noisy than agreeable in such a situation, must needs begin quarrelling with an "elegant" Captain in the hoop, as to whether they belonged to the Snobocracy or the Nobocracy, and at one time their words were literally so high that could the pair have got to close quarters the dispute would certainly have assumed a more serious character, for jammed tight together as they were in the car, the least attempt at violence would certainly have ended in discharging the whole human cargo into the railway station below. But as it was, it certainly did appear most ludicrous that two rational human beings must choose that place of all others for engaging in some paltry squabble as to the vulgar division of the human family into "Nobs" and "Snobs."

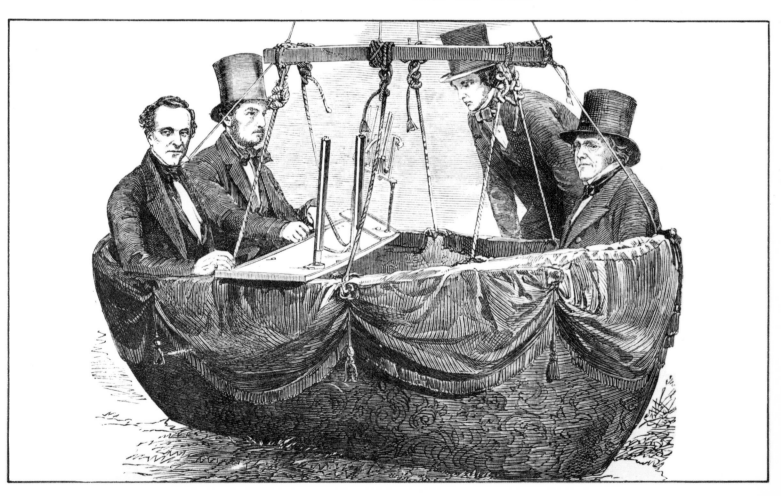

Silence, however, was soon restored by Mr. Green reminding the disputants that we were descending at a rapid rate, and it was time they began to look out for their safety.

The dyspeptic passenger, who during the dispute had evidently been suffering from another attack of nervousness, was at length terrified beyond human endurance by the gentleman who was rather worse for champagne indulging in even warmer language than he had yet given vent to.

"For mercy sake don't swear up here, my good man," shivered out the poor invalid, "Wait till you get down below, if you must swear. We are always in the hands of Providence; but up here, it strikes me, that our lives are literally hanging by a thread."

The collapsing of the bottom part of the balloon to which Mr. Green here drew our attention as evidence of the rate at which we were descending, soon restored order, and made every one anxious to attend to the directions of the aeronaut. We could now hear the sounds of "Ah bal-loon" again rising from the ground and following in our wake, telling us that at the small villages on our way the people were anxiously looking for our descent. A bag of ballast was entrusted to one of the passengers to let fall at given signal, while Green himself stood with the grapnel ready to loose immediately he came to a fitting spot. Presently the signal for the descent of the ballast was given, and as it dropped it was curious to watch it fall; the earth had seemed almost at our feet as the car swept over the fields, but so long was the heavy bag in getting to the ground that, as the eye watched it fall and fall, the mind was filled with amazement at the height the balloon was still in the air. Suddenly the sound as of a gun announced that the bag had struck the soil, and then we were told all to sit low down in the car and hold fast, and scarcely had we obeyed the orders given than the car was suddenly fiercely jerked half round, and all within it thrown one on top of another; immediately after this, bump went the bottom of the car on the ground giving us so violent a shake that it seemed as if every limb in the body had been simultaneously dislocated. Now the balloon pitched on to its side, and lay on the ground struggling with the wind, rolling about, heaving like a huge whale in the agonies of death.

"For heaven's sake! hold fast," shouted Mr. Green, as we were dashed up and down in the car, all rolling one on the other, with each fresh lurch of the giant machine stretched on the ground before us, and from which we could hear the gas roaring from the valve, like the blast to a furnace.

"Sit still, all of you, I say!" roared our pilot, as we saw some one endeavouring to leave the car.

Again we were pitched right on end, and the bottom of the car shifted into a ditch, the water of which bubbled up through the wicker work of the car, and I, unlucky wight, who was seated in that part to which the concussions were mostly confined, soon began to feel that I was quietly sitting in a pool of water.

To move, however, was evidently to peril not only one's own life, but that of all the other passengers, and still no one came to us, for we had fallen in a swamp, which we afterwards found out was Pirbright-common, situate some half-dozen miles from Guildford.

Presently, however, to our great delight, some hundred drab-smocked countrymen appeared, almost as if by magic, round the edges of the car; for some little time they were afraid to touch, but at last they got a firm hold of it, and we were one after another extricated from our seats.

To tell the remainder of the adventure would be tame and dull; suffice it, after some two hours' labour, the aerial machine, car, grapnels, and all, was rolled and packed up in a cart, and thus transported, an hour after midnight, to Guildford; the voyagers journeying to the same town in a tilted cart, delighted with their trip, and listening to the many curious adventures of the veteran aeronaut who had successfully piloted them and some hundred others through the air; and who, now that the responsibilities of our lives no longer rested in his hands, seemed a thoroughly different man: before he was taciturn, and almost irritable when spoken to; and now he was garrulous, and delighting us with his intelligence, his enterprise, his enthusiasm, and his courtesy. Indeed, long shall all remember the pleasant night we passed with the old ethereal pilot on his 500th ascent with the Royal Nassau Balloon.

(September, 1852)

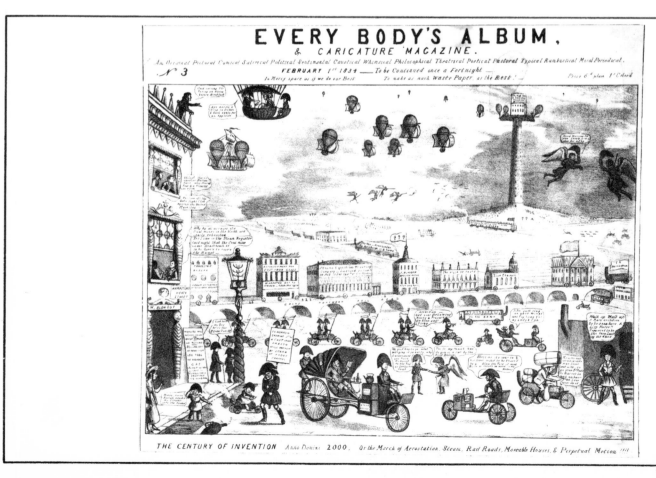

86

My Tempestuous Voyage

Mrs. Graham

Women, surprising as it may seem, have played an important role in the history of ballooning and the exploits of such as Mrs. Sage, Madame Blanchard and Mrs. Graham thrilled the public throughout Europe. One of these good ladies Mrs. Margaret Graham (1821-1880) has left us an account of a most dramatic flight and despite its brevity, the report captures all the delight and dangers of ballooning. The brave Mrs. Graham sustained severe burns on her face and hands as a result of this disaster, but was back in the air again less than one month later!

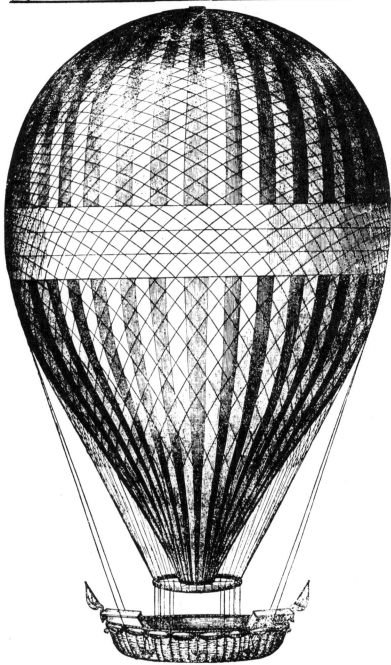

ISLINGTON
VAUXHALL.

MRS. GRAHAM,
WILL MAKE HER 35th
BALLOON ASCENT,
FROM THE GROUNDS OF THE
ROSEMARY BRANCH TAVERN,
Hoxton Bridge, Islington,
On MONDAY, August 14th,
On which occasion she will have the Honor to be Accompanied in her

Voyage, by the
COLONEL of her GRACIOUS MAJESTY'S
LUMBER TROOP.

A Variety of Entertainments of a superior description, for which see
small bills,
ADMISSION 1s.   CHILDREN 6d.

J. W. PEEL, Printer, 9, New Cut Lambeth,

I entered the car in the Cremorne Gardens, London, just after ten o'clock, at which time the wind had increased and the gas, which during the period of inflation had been considerably expanded under the sun's rays, had by this time greatly condensed, in consequence of the heavy rain, which caused an augmentation in the weight of the netting and apparatus.

The consequence was, that the balloon, which previously carried up five persons, would now only take myself, allowing for the weight of fireworks (75 lb.), the tackle of which was not attached by the advice of Mr. Simpson, the proprietor, he fearing that if the firework came in contact with the trees they might become deranged, and cause some accident to myself. The result proved the correctness of his determination, as, with an ascending power of 80 lb., I still scarcely cleared the trees.

Continuing to ascend, I speedily lost trace of the metropolis, although I could distinctly hear the rolling of carriages beneath me, which continued about a quarter of an hour, when the sound seemed lost in distance.

I now commenced descending, which I gradually did until I heard the signal of a railway train and saw some few lights; but the night being extremely dark, it was impossible to form any conjecture at to my whereabouts. I at length touched the ground, and the wind still increasing, was carried over several fields, where the grapnel took a firm hold in a ditch; and for half an hour I continued shouting as loud as I could for help, but to no purpose.

Meanwhile, I kept the valve open to its full extent, rolling about all the while, the car at times completely turning over, and giving me plenty of trouble to retain my hold. At length, police constable 305 came over the fields to my assistance, and held on to the car.

For at least twenty minutes I had no other help; but, at length additional assistance arrived, and I continued emptying the balloon.

Upon walking around to see if the valve was open a man indiscreetly came behind me with a light, which coming in contact with the escaping gas, instantaneously ignited, giving forth a volume of flame which resembled the dome of St. Paul's on fire: the effect of the sudden combustion of from 8000 to 10,000 cubic feet of gas was terrific.

August, 1850

GRAND

Aerostatic Fete

AT

AYLESBURY.

Balloon Ascent,

Under the patronage of ACTON TINDAL, Esq., Lord of the Manor.

Mr. C. GREEN,

Aeronaut to the

ROYAL GARDENS, VAUXHALL,

And Proprietor of the

GREAT NASSAU BALLOON,

With which he performed the memorable Continental Trip

FROM LONDON TO NASSAU, IN GERMANY,

A distance of

580 MILES, in 18 HOURS,

Respectfully announces to the Inhabitants and Visitors of Aylesbury, and its Vicinity, that
he purposes making his 416th Ascent on

Wednesday, July 11, 1849,

WITH HIS ROYAL VICTORIA

BALLOON,

With which he had the honour to ascend from Cambridge, in the presence of her Majesty,
his Royal Highness Prince Albert, the Duke of Wellington, Sir Robert Peel, and other
distinguished persons, at his Royal Highness Installation in July last.

This stupendous Aerostatic Machine is formed with 1,200 yards of Silk, manufactured for
the express purpose, in alternate gores of Crimson and Gold, with a Zone or Belt, on which
is inscribed " Royal Victoria," in Gold Letters three feet high, with Crowns and other
National Emblems. It measures 120 feet in circumference, contains 200,000 gallons of Gas,
and, with the Car attached, is 66 feet high.

The Ascent will take place from

A SPACIOUS MEADOW

Belonging to

Mr. T. J. HINDS, of the Black Swan Inn,

CAMBRIDGE-STREET, AYLESBURY.

PROGRAMME.

To afford the company an opportunity of inspecting the Balloon, its splendid Car, and
appendages, the doors will be opened at Two o'Clock. At Five o'Clock the Grand Ascent
of Mr. Green and companions will leave the earth with the Royal Victoria; and, at a
considerable elevation,

A PARACHUTE, CONTAINING A LIVING ANIMAL,

Will be launched from the Car, which will descend in safety within the Paddock, provided
the weather will permit.

During the inflation of the Balloon,

THE ROYAL THAME BRASS BAND

WILL PLAY SEVERAL AIRS AND OVERTURES.

Tickets of admission, to witness the inflation, attaching the car, and the immediate ascent
from the earth, One Shilling each, to be had at the *Bucks Herald* Printing-office, Temple-
street, Aylesbury.

For the accommodation of select visitors, more particularly ladies, a space will be fenced
off, commanding the most eligible view of the inflation and ascent: admission, One Shilling
extra each person. Children, Half-price.

The Balloon, partially inflated with gas, together with the Car and its appendages, will be
exhibited in the Meadow the day prior to the ascent. Admission, Sixpence each.

Geo. De Fraine, Printer, Bucks Chronicle Office, Church-street, Aylesbury.

Published 1830. by S. Gans Southampton St Strand,

AN ELEVATED SUBJECT.

"Far from the busy world remove'd, how peaceful is their lot"!!

The end of Mrs. Graham's 'tempestuous journey' in August 1850. Moments after she had scrambled clear when alighting at Booker's Field in Edmonton (left), Mrs. Graham, "Her Majesty's Aeronaute" as she was called, saw her balloon catch fire and be completely destroyed by the flames. As a result of this loss a subscription was opened to provide her with a new craft.

Disaster again befell the intrepid Mrs. Graham in June 1851 when she attempted a flight with her husband from Batty's Hippodrome in crowded Kensington, London. The balloon had hardly been released when it struck a flag pole and the silken envelope was torn. Nevertheless it cleared the buildings and continued to rise until over Piccadilly when it again dipped and struck a chimney stack. The balloon then collapsed completely and its two passengers were thrown onto the roof where Mr. Graham, a man of 66, broke both his collar and breast bone. Fortunately both were quickly rescued by the police who had been following their erratic progress (right).

Perhaps the most famous of the women aeronauts — indeed she was the first professional female balloonists — was Madame Blanchard, wife of Jean Pierre Blanchard. Like her husband she was totally committed to the new art and found it a great relief from her almost paranoic hatred of noise. She made her first solo voyage in 1805 and in 1810 took a balloon up to celebrate Napoleon's marriage festivities in Paris (below). Madame Blanchard became a great favourite with Europeans and her popularity was only really seriously challenged by Eliza Garnerin, the niece of Andre Garnerin, the parachutist, who also made daring jumps from balloons, Disaster eventually overtook Madame Blanchard on July 16 1819 when her balloon caught fire and she plunged to her death on the rooftops of Paris (opposite).

Le ballon de Mᵐᵉ Blanchard, lors de l'entrée de Louis XVIII à Paris
D'après une gouache de Hüe, conservée au Musée de Versailles

The THREE FAVORITE AERIAL TRAVELLERS.

Vincent Lunardi Esq.͠ first Aeronaut in England.

George Biggin Esq.͠

and M.ͬˢ Sage first English Female Aerial Traveller.

Publish'd June 28.ᵗʰ 1785. by E. Wyatt next door to the Pantheon, Oxford Street.

A Lady's Balloon Ride over an Ocean of Flame

Rufus Gibbon Wells

In America, women were also proving their prowess with balloons, and one of the Country's leading aeronauts, Rufus Gibbon Wells (1816-1896) recorded this account of a most exciting voyage. Wells himself made a number of outstanding trips in Europe—including the first balloon journey over the Apennines—and several hundred ascents in America. He was also the leading figure behind the scheme to build a 100 m.p.h. "Great Steel Air Ship" in Boston in 1889.

During the winter of 1858 I visited the beautiful Southern city of New Orleans, where I witnessed the balloon ascents of an intelligent and intrepid lady aeronaut from one of the Western States. She had made several daring ascents alone in the West and the South, and had now determined to show the Creoles of the Crescent City some of her courageous feats.

Her manager obtained the use of the Congo Square, in the French part of New Orleans, for the ascents, and had the place well surrounded by a high canvas. Her balloon was inflated by gas from the city gasworks. As the citizens were very fond of exciting amusements, and it being the first time that any lady-aeronaut had visited them, they turned out on masse to patronise the enterprise. It was a splendid day when she made her first ascent, accompanied by her manager, a writer for the Press.

When she flung out the stars and stripes to the breeze the band played the national air, and the multitude gave cheer upon cheer until the balloon had reached five thousand feet above the winding Mississippi, "the Father of Waters." This glorious stream could be distinctly seen extending its many channels to the Gulf of Mexico. The sides of the river were lined for the six miles of its wharfs with vessels decorated with flags of all nations. The engineers of the river steamboats up and down the stream, and of the

locomotives rushing in and out of the city, on seeing the balloon sailing proudly above the earth blew their shrill whistles loud and long. The old battle-field below the city, where General Andrew Jackson won his famous victory, through which he afterwards became President of the United States, could be seen on the opposite side of the river. The old French cathedral, the St. Charles Hotel, Lafayette and Jackson Squares, and hundreds of splendid gardens with magnolia and orange trees, and choice flowers, formed a charming panorama worthy for the human eyes to feast upon.

The balloon was carried by a light breeze westwards Lake Ponchertrain. The aeronauts were compelled to either descend in a large swamp or make an attempt to cross the lake, which is thirty miles wide. As night was coming on they made up their minds to descend in the swamp. They however knew this to be a hazardous undertaking, for the swamps in the Southern States are usually infected with reptiles.

They landed among the moss-covered cypress-trees, where the water was about two feet deep. Some negroes saw them from the shore of the lake and went into the swamp to help them out. They planned to carry the lady in the basket to dry ground, and to take the gentlemen on the back of a strong negro. The balloon was committed to the care of some trusty black men, who with much difficulty removed it from the trees and returned it to the city. The aerial travellers, now fairly on their novel journey from the balloon, were becoming quite jovial over their adventure, when their fears of reptiles in the swamp was suddenly revived by a splashing sound in the water near by. But a moment more, and crash went the jaws of an alligator on the leg of one of the men carrying the basket. With a cry of pain he was dragged down into the water. In an instant all hands, with their clubs, and the help of the dogs, yelping and barking, fell into fierce conflict with the

monster, which was finally killed by a ball through the eye from the revolver of the journalist. A rope was put round the body of the dead alligator and it was dragged out of the swamp along with the party. The man who was caught by the reptile had the fibula, or small bone of his leg broken. He was carried by his companions. A large dog was caught by another alligator and devoured just as the company was starting from the place of the accident.

Arrangements were soon made for another ascent by the lady from the same square. On this occasion the manager, to interest the multitude of spectators while the balloon was being inflated with gas, arranged to have a debate between the lady-aeronaut and Mr. J.B. Anderson, a young Kentucky lawyer, who was employed as bookkeeper for a large firm (Peek and Co., agents for Wheeler and Wilson's sewing machines, on Canal Street). The subject of the debate was "Woman's Rights"—then a popular subject in the North, but little discussed in the South.

Miss W——, the young lady, was a graduate of a Western college, which had for president the celebrated educator Horace Mann, of Massachusette. She was a good debater and a capital speaker, having a strong voice that could be heard by the vast multitude present. Mr. Anderson being quite an orator, and coming from a State famous for such distinguished orators as Henry Clay and Thomas Marshall, it was thought by the majority of the people that he would easily win the debate. I was well acquainted with both of the debaters, and therefore took great interest in the result of the discussion, as well as in the aerial flight which was to follow. Miss W—— opened the argument and spoke for half an hour in favour of Woman's Rights. Mr. Anderson then spoke for three-quarters of an hour on the negative side of the question, when Miss W—— closed the debate by speaking another half hour. The decision of the judges was in favour of the lady's arguments. Miss W—— received much praise from the New Orleans Press for the able manner in which she conducted the debate, and for her triumph over the Kentucky lawyer.

On my visit to New Orleans in 1884, to the World's Exposition, I was surprised to learn from a son of Mr. Peck that J.B. Anderson was the father of the celebrated actress Miss Mary Anderson. I well remember that his black

piercing eyes, jet black hair, and tall manly figure; and recalling the appearance of his talented daughter as I had seen her in her profession, I could very well trace their likeness. Mr. Anderson became an officer in Confederate army, and was killed when the Northern army, under General Grant, took Vicksburg. Little did he ever think or even dream that his daughter by her talents and perseverance would become one of the best known women in the world, and accumulate more than a million dollars in Europe and America by her unprecedented success in her profession—more especially in London.

On the second ascent the crowd was even greater than on the first, and the enthusiasm wilder. The manager again accompanied Miss W—— on the trip. The wind was from the south, which carried the balloon towards Lake Ponchertrain, as on the first voyage. They decided not to land again in the swamp, but to continue on and make a journey, if possible of several hundred miles to the north. Night came on while they were passing over the lake. Steamers could be seen, like beautiful illuminated palaces, traversing the water, and the stars shone brilliantly overhead. The balmy atmosphere lulled the senses of the travellers into a state of repose—very grateful after the excitement of the day. Quietly contemplating the scene below them, they were startled on reaching the opposite shore of the lake to find great fires raging in the forests of more than one hundred miles in extent, which partially cover the State of Louisiana.

Although they were at the height of one mile above the earth they could hear distinctly the roaring and raging of the dreadful conflagration. Tall trees all ablaze came crashing to the ground with thundering sound. In places the smoke rose as from the crater of a mighty volcano. Then a whole sea of fire would burst upon the view of the bewildered voyagers. It was fearful to look upon such a scene, and to think of the possibility of coming down into this glowing furnace with a balloon full of explosive gas. It was impossible to descend without meeting certain death anywhere in the neighbourhood of the fires, for among the dry pine-trees, with their resinous exhudations, fire spreads with such wonderful rapidity, and the inhabitants fleeing before it, the region is soon left desolate. Not a human being could be seen anywhere as far as the travellers could see. Cattle overtaken by the fire were heard bellowing in their fright, and the screams of panthers and other wild animals came from many places.

Onward went the balloon, with its passengers wondering what would be their fete, when the anchor, which was suspended one hundred feet beneath the car, caught in the top of a tree on a hill and suddenly ended their voyage by sending the balloon against another tree, in which the net became entangled, leaving them suspended about sixty feet from the ground between the two trees. Here they were forced to remain from midnight until morning, rocked by the breeze in the tops of the trees, which put them in mind of the good old nursery rhyme—

> *"Rock-a-by baby on the tree top,*
> *When the wind blows the cradle will rock,*
> *When the bough breaks the cradle will fall,*
> *Then down goes baby, cradle and all."*

It happened that the car was spacious enough to allow them to lie down to rest, if not to sleep. They could then sing the good old lovers' tune with more truth than poetry—

> *"We won't go home till morning,"* etc.

The barking of dogs and cow-bells could be heard during the night, which indicated that they had arrived near some settlement in the forest. In the morning the manager made a swing seat out of some strong ropes and let Miss W——

down to the ground. She went off, revolver in hand, to explore the surroundings, with the hope of finding someone to help. About a quarter of a mile distant she saw a house. On going to it she found it to be the home of Dr. McQuin. The doctor on learning her circumstances went with her to the balloon, taking with him some of his slaves, who assisted her compagnon de voyage to descend from his elevated position to terra firma. It happened that they had, luckily, just passed over the great forest, one hundred miles in extent, and had reached cultivated land.

The doctor invited them to go with him to his house and have some refreshments, although they had plenty with them in the car. He thought it would be a great curiosity to his neighbours and their slaves to see the balloon hanging in the trees. Everybody was informed in the region for many miles around, and came to the place and received hospitality from Dr. McQuin, who was a rich planter. It was made a holiday for all the slaves in the district. It required the strong arms of several slaves to cut down three large pine-trees to get the balloon free. It was considerably injured tearing against the branches of the trees.

It was many miles from any telegraph-station, so it was required a few days to get the news of the descent at New Orleans. It was thought that they had been carried into the Gulf of Mexico and lost. The descent was made about two hundred miles from New Orleans, in Pike county, Mississippi.

In America, too, women balloonists made news. The most charming of the stories concerning them was of the lady enthusiast who chose to be married in a balloon at Cincinnati in 1874 (opposite, left). The most alarming was the narrow escape of the two young women who became entangled in the trail rope of a balloon as it was ascending from a fair in North Carolina in 1871. Fortunately the aeronauts, who were professional balloonists, quickly spotted their unexpected passengers and pulled them to safety. An un-named lady aeronaut was dramatically rescued from the sea·off the coast of Boston the following year when her balloon developed a sudden leak and plunged into the ocean (above, left). A fourth lady of the skies was injured, though not seriously, when two over enthusiastic helpers tipped her from her basket in Connecticut in 1880. The illustration here is taken from a lady's magazine of the period which used the incident to condemn ballooning as "not the occupation for demure young ladies of good breeding."

Ballooning Broadsheet

Broadsheets on ballooning were immensely popular in both Britain and on the Continent. They were sold for a fraction of a penny by travelling sellers and sung or recited throughout the taverns and bawdy houses of Europe. Here is a typical example from the end of the Eighteenth Century which originally appeared with a number of gaudy red and yellow illustrations now sadly so faded as to make reproduction of all but one impossible.

Should war again break out
As is not a doubt
With some that it may happen soon;
The French will invade us
Their troops will parade us
Brought over in an Air Balloon.

Their ships will appear,
Not in water but in air,
And come in a twinkling down,
From Calais to Dover,
How quickly they'll be over,
Blown up in an Air Balloon.

The Balloon at War

Henry Coxwell

Henry Coxwell (1819-1900) was one of the most prominent of British Balloonists and apart from his great skill was also a visionary concerning the future of aviation. In this article published in 1889 he introduces us to the use of balloons in warfare and cites examples from Britain, Europe and America.

MANY articles have appeared on this subject, but they are mostly concise compilations as to the dates of the employment of war balloons, and there is yet wanting a more simple and systematic arrangement of the order and particulars under which the respective balloons figured in early aeronautic history.

I have endeavoured to supply these requirements and to add a few practical and critical observations as to the merits and faults of the various equipments and plans from an aeronautic standpoint; as this kind of treatment may interest military aeronauts, and assist civilians who are studying the matter, and it may also prove more attractive to general readers who like to know what professional men have to say (in friendly rivalry) as to the ideas of naval and military officers, who have devoted attention to ballooning.

On the other hand military men, the young especially, who are apt to conclude that veterans know very little compared with modern tactitians, may find that in this speciality they are somewhat mistaken, and that ballooning is not to be "picked up," so to speak, without having a regular and legitimate schooling in an art which so very few understand.

*"One Science only will one genius fit,
So vast is art, so narrow human wit."*

The inventive genius of the French may be traced no less than their intrepidity in their early efforts to apply the balloon to purposes of warfare.

In the year 1793, a scientific committee was formed in Paris with this object, when it was suggested that balloons should be used both for attack and defence, and for ascertaining the movement of armies in the field, and to get at the strength of fortified places.

Here was a clear and comprehensive plan for a new departure in military science which the leading nations of Europe have been slow in imitating.

A great deal of doubt and ridicule have been cast upon those (myself included), who, in different countries had the courage of their convictions to urge such a movement upon the attention of those in power.

Austria, whose forces first faced a war balloon at the battle of Fleurus, directed her government not to neglect a bird's-eye view of the enemy.

Russia took up the idea pretty early.

Italy followed suit.

Germany was slow to move in the air, but has been steady and scientific in carrying out her projects.

Old England, proverbially averse to new fangled notions,

Behold an odd Fight, two odd Nations between,
Such odd Fighting as this was never yet seen:—

The B
BAL

N.º 69 in S.ʰ Pauls Church Yard, London.

'LE

N S.

But such Fights will be common (as Dunce to feel Rod)
In the Year of One Thousand eight Hundred and odd.

resisted all overtures even from an experienced aeronaut for many years, pooh-poohing this kind of feather-brained mode of strategy as at that period imagined.

At last, after experiments had been made by Colonel Beument and myself at Aldershot and Woolwich, a balloon corps was formed and permitted to try their hand with calico balloons.

This new force, however, ignoring the first instructors most persistently, ventured to teach the British army without recognized balloonists to aid them; but one day, in an unfortunate hour, a war balloon, while taking a preliminary canter, not, of course, in an official capacity, dashed off on a dark December evening to sea, with an enterprising and much lamented member of Parliament, who knew no fear, but had a poor chance of being rescued from a watery grave.

The process of inflation lasted for thirty-six to forty hours. I may here call attention to the decided improvement which appears to have been made in the generation and storage of hydrogen gas for the English balloon force. Compressed gas is now supplied at Chatham in metal receivers, which can be sent abroad, as it was to Suakim. This plan has its advantages and difficulties. It must be very expensive, and the weight of the cylinders is an objection where every ounce of impedimenta has to be sometimes thought of.

The French balloons were made of silk, and so efficiently varnished that they retained the gas for two to three months.

In this important element we are behind the French, as mere calico was the first fabric used in the construction of the Woolwich balloons, and though professional aeronauts for public ascents may sometimes resort to cotton balloons, still for military objects, silk, although the most costly, is, I should say, the lightest, strongest, tightest, and best.

We must allow for considerable exaggeration in the much vaunted holding powers of the original French balloons, and, for the matter of that, for the latest productions as well, both in England and on the continent I must include the Channel balloonists.

It is all very well to talk and write about such a volatile substance as hydrogen, or even coal gas, remaining good for three months or a month. Aeronants deny it.

Will a volume of the lightest known fluid be fit for much after being a fortnight or even a week in either a silk, skin, or so called india-rubber envelopes.

Until ballooning is divested of much that is absurd, untruthful, and misleading, real progress will be slow.

The balloon "Entreprenant" which was sent to the army of the north was only twenty-seven feet in diameter, and its lifting power was 500 pounds. It was held fast by two ropes which were attached to some extra network at the equator; but considering that in those days the network did not cover much more than half of the balloon, we should not fail to notice that at present balloons are enveloped in much more extensive and elongated nets which protect the lower hemisphere, and prevent the escape of the balloon unless the network gives way. It is generally made of thicker cord below, so that this danger is more guarded against than it was in the year 1794.

The army of the Meuse-Sambre had the "Celeste" balloon, while the "Hercule" and "Intrepide" were sent to the Rhine-Moselle.

The recent Naval Jubilee Review reminds one how interesting it would be could the aerial fleet of the last century be inspected by the side of the latest style of war ballons that England has produced.

I am not at all sure that comparisons would be in our favour. Fancy the British army under an amateur!

On June 18th, when Coutelle reconnoitred the Austrian position, the enemy fired at his balloon as it was ascending and descending.

From Maubeuge it was taken to Charleroi, floating at such a height as to permit cavalry and other troops to pass beneath.

At the battle of Fleurus, in Belgium, on June 26th, 1794, two ascents were made, each of about four or five hours, notwithstanding a strong wind; the success of the French was said to be generally due to observations from this balloon, as all movements were reported.

Then, after this calamity, the British balloon force languished, but not for long, as war clouds were to be seen in the East, where military balloons should have been sent, particularly to Alexandria, but they were not, nor to other places in which Lord Wolseley has himself admitted that they might have proved very useful.

Our own progress at home and the activity displayed on the continent form an instructive contrast, but if we want to ascertain and compare the present with the past we must go back to the year 1793, and follow on chronologically.

The Committee of Public Safety (an excellent kind of committee for London adoption) gave their approval on condition that the gas should be prepared without using sulphuric acid, as sulphur could ill be spared on account of its being so much needed for the production of gunpowder.

Guyton de Morveau showed that water could be decomposed by being forced over red hot metal and borings in a retort, the oxygen being thus separated from the hydrogen which was alone required for an inflation.

Experiments at Meudon were instituted under the direction of Guyton de Morveau, Coutelle, and Conte. Their report led to the formation of a company to be named the *Aerostiers*, who boasted a captain, a sergeant-major, one sergeant, two corporals, and twenty men.

Coutelle was captain, and the *Aerostiers* went to Meudon to be practised in the aeronautic art. After the preliminary experiments Coutelle was sent off to General Jourdan at Maubeuge with material for the inflation, but he arrived at the moment when General Chasal was under arrest for being involved in a plot to deliver the place to the enemy. Jourdan threatened to shoot him as a spy, but he softened down, as De Fonvielle relates, when he saw that Coutelle was no in the least disconcerted, and ended by congratulating him on his zeal in the defence of his country.

The balloon corps contained in its ranks, as indeed some of the modern associations do, some rather singular individuals. We are told in "Adventures in the Air" of a priest of Montmorency, whom the Reign of Terror had driven to take refuge in the camp, but who only waited the advent of more peaceable times to resume his cassock.

We may also mention Selles de Beauchamp, who entered the corps under the name of Cavalier Albert, and who rose to the rank of officer, and left interesting memoirs on the experiences of military balloonists.

The father of Beauchamp, an officer in one of the royal regiments, was seriously wounded in Piedmont, where two of his brothers were killed; he retired, moreover, and died in 1781, leaving a child six years old, who, two years later, lost his mother also. As an orphan of fortune, as soon as he was old enough, he was sent to the Harcourt College, where he was treated as a youth of quality.

His tutor adopted zealously the revolutionary cause, while Beauchamp stuck to the Court party. The latter, in attempting to leave the country, was arrested and sent to the army of the Loire, but rather than join it he engaged among the military balloonists, of whose life, but for him, we should have known nothing, for the memoirs of

One of the first people to appreciate the value of balloons in warfare was Louis Bernard Guyton de Morveau (left), chancellor of the Academy of Dijon and a contemporary of the Montgolfiers. In 1793 he pointed out to the new French Republican government who were faced with internal disorder and external enemies the "infinite usefulness" of balloons to observe the opposing forces and direct strategy, apart from dropping missiles on them. Morveau had in fact been experimenting with balloons for a number of years and was particularly interested in devising methods of controlling the direction of their flight. In the second contemporary print (below), Morveau is seen making his most famous journey from Dijon in 1784 in the company of the Abbe Berteau to test the oars and sails he had devised. Strong winds affected the balloon quite considerably, but Morveau did claim a certain success for his system of navigation although no-one was subsequently prepared to utilise it further.

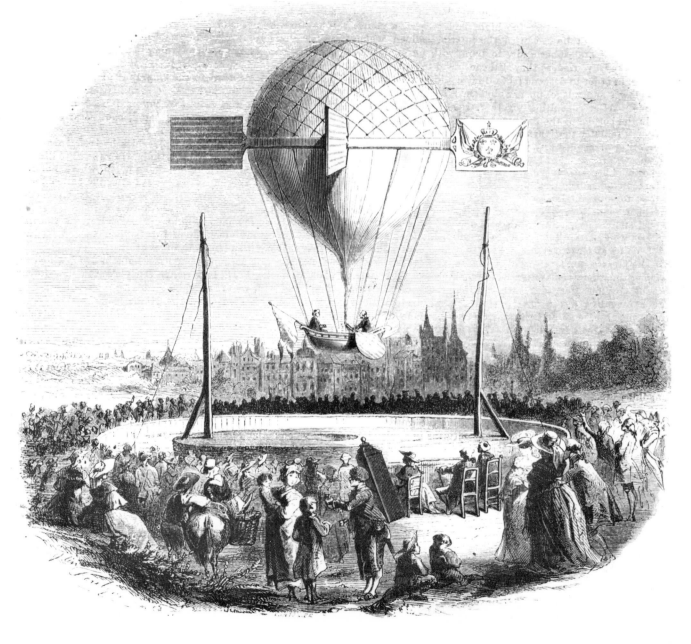

The use of the balloon for military reconnaissance first took place during the battle at Maubeuge on June 2 1794. The French forces sent up the craft, "Entreprenant" and from its position above the lines its two occupants sent down reports of the enemy movements. In charge of this operation was Jean Marie-Joseph Coutelle (left) a captain in the Army of the North and prior to the war a chemist. Earlier that year he had been appointed by Napoleon to form a balloon company, the *Aerostiers,* and into its ranks he introduce men specialised in chemistry, sketching, carpentry and masonry. This unit, the first air corps in history, scored perhaps its greatest success at the Battle of Fleurus on June 26 when Coutelle remained aloft in the "Entreprenant" for nine hours and dropped a string of messages to General Jourdan's forces below about the movements of the Austrian invader. The old print reproducd here graphically captures the battle, while the second picture shows Captain Coutelle at work in his basket despite the attentions of enemy cannons. The success of the *Aerostiers* inspired military ballooning as an art and it has continued ever since.

Coutelle, though very valuable from a scientific point of view, are too laconic, and enter into no details.

To these various characters Coutelle added a certain number of mechanics, whose services were indispensable. His first lieutenant, Delaunnay, was formerly a master mason, and proved useful in the construction of furnaces, for it required no less than 12,000 bricks to build the furnace for the manufacture of gas.

The balloonists were again brought into requisition in the campaign of 1795. The "Entreprenant" withstood an amount of buffeting which would shatter a modern balloon to shreds; we are reminded of this by a high French authority, and I am not prepared to dispute this bold assertion, when we remember of what material some of the latest war ballons are composed.

The strain on Coutelle's balloon was lessened by attaching the cable to horses and men, rather than to fixed objects.

Of course it was; there are secrets in every art, and I may here mention a case in point as to the danger of a too rigid holdfast, which happened to my large balloon, which I made at my own cost for The British Association Experiments, in the year 1862.

While the committee at Wolverhamption, which included Professor Tyndall, Lord Wrottesley, Dr. Lee, Mr. Glaisher, and others, were watching the inflation during a high wind, I left the grounds for a short time, the balloon being in charge of my assistants, who were manoeuvring at the nozzle of the lower opening, as that is a part requiring much care, and will not admit, without great risk, of being held too fast; the late Colonel Sykes, M.P., considered that if a crow-bar were driven in the ground, and the cord were attached, it would prevent the men from being rolled over occasionally, and his idea was put to the test.

I was surprised to observe from a distance, that the balloon had been badly torn, and could not account for it until I returned and saw that the neck valve had been pulled completely away. Had it been kept as I left it, with a give and take movement to obviate a sudden snatch, the balloon would have escape injury.

It is really astonishing how the same ideas occur to all amateurs and novices. Those who read much about aerostatics must have noticed that a strong resemblance in these notions is constantly to be observed; they one and all begin with the valve and have ever since I can remember.

They all want to try india-rubber and other complicated springs instead of the rat-trap principle, which is so very simple, and cannot well fail to act in all weathers, whereas india-rubber will relax in heat, and beadings and other additions will swell and contract in the framework, if of wood, according to atmospheric changes; but the plan, which experienced aeronauts know to be the safest, is almost sure to be cast aside until an accident, as I have already pointed out, induces beginners to fall back upon the approved plan.

Then again, the varnishes are wrong, Mr. A. or Mr. M. has a varnish which is perfectly impermeable, the old stories and new pretensions are reiterated, while the old stager knows very well that there are objections to most of the new fancies, and that the colours and oils he has used are like those of the old masters in painting, not so easily to be surpassed, particularly in the present day, when most pigments are so impure and adulterated.

Thirdly, the grapnels are all wrong, but if the ropes and balloon equipments of early days were to be put side by side with many of the accessories of modern appliances, I believe the balance would be in favour of the experts of the last generation.

In 1796, the "Intrepide" was sent to the army of the Danube; a fifth balloon was prepared for the army of Italy, but for some reason it was never sent out.

In the year 1798, Napoleon took a balloon equipment to Egypt, but unfortunately for the French, the English managed to capture the ship which contained the apparatus.

After this, the *Aerostiers* seem to have gradually died out of notice, and the balloons were sold in 1804.

It was said that the dissolution of the corps was due more immediately to the displeasure of Napoleon at the performance of a balloon which ascended at his coronation, with a large crown suspended beneath it, which travelled all the way to Rome, and deposited part of the crown on the tomb of Nero.

After the Peace of Amiens was concluded in March 1802, military aeronauts were less heard of, while professional and scientific air explorers came more prominently into notice.

In 1812, the Russians constructed a huge balloon at Moscow, which was to hover over the French army and rain forth shells and explosives, but their expectations rose higher than their balloons, which refused to move off the ground.

The French soldiers found this in the Castle of Voronzoff bearing many thousand pounds of gunpowder, which were to have been launched upon them.

General Count Philip de Segur says:— "This prodigious balloon was constructed by command of Alexander, not far from Moscow, under the direction of a German artificer."

In 1815 a balloon reconnaissance was made at Antwerp, and in 1826 the subject was again mooted by the French, and a balloon was sent to Algiers, but it was never disembarked.

The Russians are said to have tried experiments at Sebastopol in 1854.

The French again used balloons in the Italian campaign of 1859; they employed the civilian aeronaut Godard, and a useful ascent was made the day before Solferino in a fire balloon.

When the Civil War in America broke out several balloons were used in the operations. On October 4th, 1861, an aeronaut named La Montaine ascended from McClellan's camp on the Potomac; he was enabled to make observation of their position and movements, and afterwards returned to his own lines and communicated results which were declared to be of the utmost importance.

Later on the Federals instituted a regular balloon corps, of which Colonel Beaumont, R.E., wrote an interesting account in the Royal Engineer Papers. The balloons were of two sizes, one of 13,000 cubic feet capacity, the other double that size, but the large size was found most suitable, a fact which our military balloonists should not overlook in their desire to possess very light and small balloons for easy transport.

The American balloons were made of the best silk, the upper part being composed of three or four thicknesses; this was capable of retaining sufficient gas for an ascent a fortnight after inflation, a statement which can more readily be credited than the French accounts about preserving it for *three months.*
Hydrogen was used for inflation, and generated in the old-fashioned way with scrap iron and sulphuric acid.

Two of the American balloons and two generators were taken each on a four horsed waggon, with one two horsed acid cart.

Earthworks could be distinguished at a distance of five miles, while the piquets and supports of the enemy were distinctly seen. A telegraphic wire was sometimes attached to the balloon, so that the aeronaut could at once communicate with the general, or even, as was done one time, to the Government at Washington. Some photographs were also taken of the enemy's position.

The aeronaut and the general each had maps similarly

A further use to which balloons could be put in war. After their experiences at the hands of the French, the Austrians were not slow to realise the value of the balloon and in 1849 they sent a pilotless convoy of them over the city of Venice to drop incendiary bombs on the beleagured garrison. The bombs were governed by time fuses and worked remarkably well.

(Opposite). Aerial combat as envisaged in a French periodical, circa 1850.

The elaborate balloon created especially for the celebrations to mark the coronation of Napoleon in 1804.

divided into small squares, which were numbered, whereby the communications were simplified.

The "Times" correspondent said of the battle of Chickahominy: "During the whole of the engagement, Professor Lowe's balloon hovered over the Federal lines at an altitude of 2,000 feet, and maintained successful telegraphic communication with General McClellan's head-quarters."

In an attack on Mississippi Island, No. 10, Engineer Aeronaut Allan, ascended and directed the artillery fire, communicating the effect of each shot.

In July 1862, the first military balloon experiments in England took place at Aldershot, and, as I had the honour of accomplishing them, I will leave Lieut. Baden-Powell to allude to the events in his own words.

"The aeronaut, Mr. Coxwell, was employed to bring one of his balloons which was filled at the gas works, and made several captive ascents, the highest being 2,200 feet, Colonel Beaumont said that no large movement of troops could take place within a radius of ten miles without being seen. Later on, more experiments were made, a one-inch rope being used as cable.

"When the war between France and Germany broke out, Mr. Coxwell went to manage some war balloons for the Germans. He formed two companies (two officers and forty-two men) at Cologne, and his assistant went on to Strasbourg, but that town capitulated before much service was rendered."

During the siege of Paris, balloons, it will be remembered, were made use of in a more regular and extensive manner, and with most important results.

At first, two old balloons were anchored at Montmartre and Montsouris, as observatories, to watch the Prussians. They apparently accomplished but little, although one or two new ideas were introduced. The messages from the balloons were put in a little box which was attached to the cable by a ring, so that the observations were delivered straight to those who held the rope.

Every twenty-four hours, six ascents were made, four by day, and two by night, the latter to observe the camp fires, etc., and it was proposed to use an electric search light.

When the Parisians found themselves cut off from all communication with the outer world, balloons were naturally suggested as a means of escape.

Several experienced aeronauts were in Paris as well as a few balloons.

The first aeronaut, Duruof, left in a leaky machine, which owing to its imperfect conditions, was sent up like a projectile, as we are informed by De Fonvielle. It described a parabola like that a bombshell, and by sacrificing seven hundredweight of ballast, the descent took place nineteen miles from the Place St. Pierre, in the department of Eure, not far from the Prussians, but still beyond their range.

The "Ville de Florence" took, by way of trail, the first pigeons intended for return with despatches. Paris learned with as much satisfaction as if it had been a victory, the return of the first aerial messenger.

Louis Godard had two small balloons, neither sufficient for the purpose of escape, but he fixed one below the other, and made a very successful voyage in the "Etats-Unis."

The last ready made balloon was the "Celeste," which was the first to take post cards.

The Government then ordered a number of new balloons to be at once constructed, they were turned out at the chief railway stations, which for the time being were no longer used as such.

The balloons were made of strong cambric, oiled, and of about 70,000 cubic feet capacity; they were filled with coal gas, and could carry a load of 2,000 pounds, including 600 pounds of ballast and 1,000 pounds of despatches.

The first of these bore Gambetta, he was accompanied by his intimate friend, M. Spuller. The political results of this voyage are well known.

One balloon travelled to Norway. Many were fired at, but few injured. Three balloons fell into the hands of the enemy near Paris, and two in Germany. Two were lost at sea, each manned by a sailor.

The average distance travelled was about 180 miles, and the speed varied from seven to fifty miles an hour, and in one instance, eighty miles.

During four months, sixty-six balloons left Paris, of which fifty-four were specially made by the administration of posts and telegraphs.

One hundred-and-sixty persons were carried over the Prussian lines.

Nine tons of despatches, or 3,000,000 letters were successfully conveyed to their destinations. 360 pigeons were taken up, of which, however, only fifty-seven returned to Paris, these conveyed, as Lieut. Baden-Powell reminds us, 100,000 messages.

Wilfrid de Fonvielle gives us a vivid and thrilling account of how he left Paris in a balloon.

The members of the scientific commission, he informs us, conceived the idea of sending off balloons by night. He took his departure on the 20th of November; he was apprehensive, owing to the weather, of some crushing catastrophe.

"The 'Egalite' began to show its graceful form and bright colours. The sun was shining on the golden sphere, which the wind was gracefully oscillating. I was looking on the clouds, which had a direction inclining somewhere towards Prussian soil, when I heard people shouting.

"A large hole had been made by the copper end of the pipe in the graceful fabric. It was too late to think of mending it, and of ascending afterwards before sunset."

On the following morning the weather was horrid. After many delays, owing to this cause, De Fonvielle and his companions started. They saw desolated fields, disappearing one after another. He recognized different parts where he had wandered during so many happy years. Twice the Seine was crossed, that noble Seine! where German horses will never drink! and he could see distinctly where his old balloon had been taken by German hands.

He was looking at that spot when the first shot was heard, but the balloon was more than 5,000 feet high. In less than two hours they reached Louvain.

A few days after this successful journey, another nocturnal balloon went up on a moonless night. A brave sailor, named Prince, was the sole occupant of the car.

Next day, at dawn, some fishermen on the north coast of Scotland, saw a globe disappear towards the west and sink in the ocean. A poor mother and two sisters bewailed the loss of the unfortunate waif.

In April 1879, the English Government instituted an official balloon committee, consisting of Colonel Noble, R.E., Sir F. Abel, and Captain Lee, R.E., with whom was associated Captain Elsdale, R.E., and Captain Templer, of the Middlesex Militia, the last mentioned having had considerable experience in ballooning.

Experiments were conducted at Woolwich, and four balloons were made by the Royal Engineers of specially woven fine calico, varnished.

A portable furnace and boiler for the manufacture of hydrogen gas was devised similiar in principle to the one used by the French in 1798, but the apparatus did not prove satisfactory.

In the American Civil War (1861-3) balloons also played an important role. The leading figure in this context was Thaddeus S. C. Lowe of the Union Army who devised a special signalling system for his balloon company, America's first 'air force' (opposite, top). Lowe was a colourful figure who had first come to public notice with a project for a Trans-Atlantic Flight in a balloon in 1859-60. At the outset of the Civil War he was jailed as a Union Spy but was released and went to the North where he formed a balloon company. He achieved this object despite considerable opposition and even had the indignity of being fired on by his own troops during one demonstration. Nonetheless the idea proved a success as these contemporary drawings show. In one (above, top) soldiers struggle to inflate the balloon "Eagle" during a storm, while in the second (above) in better condition the balloon "Intrepid" prepares for launching at Vienna in Virginia. The final drawing (opposite) illustrates the fore-runner of the aeroplane carrier ship — the balloon-boat which was used as the base for several observation trips at Budd's Ferry, Maryland.

And who could expect that a mere imitation after the lapse of eighty-six years, would do much good or credit to the British army. Had a competent man been appointed consulting aeronaut, he would have pointed out that the use of bricks, tiles, and red hot turnings, was resorted to in France as a neccessity when sulphur and sulphuric acid were scarce, but as none of the above named officers had ever ascended with me, or had my instructions, I could only note, with regret, what appeared to be a useless expenditure of money and time, and as to proper and suitable material, I had in my store rooms at Seaford, Sussex, a large quantity of stout, pure silk, made expressly for balloons, and could have turned out for the Government, a typical war balloon, which would have been creditable to our country, and been in every way preferable to *calico*.

A few days after the first experiment, an unforeseen adventure happened as one of the war balloons was being towed, attached to a cart.

The cable snapped and the balloon disappeared in the clouds!

In October, one of the balloons was tried free at a review on Woolwich Common, but the wind was unfavourable.

The next year, the "Crusader" figured at the Brighton volunteer review, successfully.

In September 1880, a whole company of Engineers (the 24th) went for instruction in ballooning to Aldershot, and many experiments were made.

English military ballooning, as I have pointed out received a sudden check when the "Saladin" was lost in the year 1881.

If we turn to the French, we read quite a different story. They established, in 1872, another aeronautical school. An annual grant of £10,000 was made, and since then, the establishment has increased.

Their balloons are spherical, ten metres in diameter, made of the best silk, and covered with a varnish which renders them so gas-tight, that they can remain inflated for a month. So they assert.

Twenty out of forty balloons had already been made.

For captive ascents a kite screen is used. I suggested something of this kind twenty-six years since, but I have now a more simple and safer plan, with others for signalling etc., should they ever be enquired after or wanted.

If there is one branch of modern strategy which is likely to be watched with keen interest during the next Continental war it will be that of military ballooning. For some time we have heard of such wonderful preparations in this line on the other side of the Channel that the public, both at home and abroad, will be moved by anxious expectancy to take note whether the steering gas bags and air torpedoes revolutionize warfare by developing a more easy way of striking hostile forces, namely, from a vertical position, in which they are so frequently vulnerable. The aims of those who would merely employ balloons to see what is going on behind the hills, and how their opponents are disposed. seem insufficient to satisfy the ambition of foreign engineers. A Frenchman has supplied the Russians with an air torpedo that can be directed, so we are told, with accuracy of a submarine machine. It is to take up eight hundredweight of dynamite, which can be discharged on the heads, and on the magazines and fortresses of their foes, so as to make short work with them by blowing them up sky-high without subjecting the attacking party to risk, owing to the remarkable guiding power of their aerial cruiser, which is to strike and glide away with marvellous rapidity, either as it emerges from the clouds, or springs unseen above the smoke of battle, to let fall its destructive cargo when least expected. All this sounds very terrific and smart in theory, but the question is, can it be done with the tact and certainty which we are asked to believe? From an aerostatic standpoint such an enterprise would entirely

Balloons were also made use of during the siege of Paris between September 1870 and May 1871. The cornered citizens got messages out of the city by balloons manufactured especially for the purpose, and during the period of the siege some 65 escaped carrying 164 passengers, 381 pigeons, 5 dogs and eleven tons of mail. One of those trapped in city was Victor Hugo who wrote the following account dated October 7 1780:

"This morning, while strolling, I saw a balloon at the end of a street leading to Montmartre. I approached. A sizeable crowd surrounded a staked off area.Three balloons had been inflated in this area, the largest of which was yellow, the middle one white, and the smaller, yellow and red. It was 10.30 in the morning. The weather was fine with a light southerly wind and a soft autumn sun. All of a sudden the yellow balloon took off with three men inside. Then the white balloon, also containing three men, one of whom was waving the tricolour. There was a cry of "Vive la Republique". The two balloons rose, the white one faster than the yellow, then they started to lose height; they threw out ballast but still continued to drop. They disappeared behind the Butte-Montmartre and were forced to descend on the Saint Denis plain. Either they were overloaded or there was not enough wind . . ."

depend upon aerial navigation having been solved. Certain inventors avow, and perhaps imagine, that this consummation has been settled already by those preliminary canters near Paris of which we heard so much two years since. Now, it is not for me, or any other practical man, to say that the pretensions put forth for "the conquest of the air" are visionary; but this I do say, that the alleged movements of the cigar-shaped balloons have not warranted us in concluding that the art of steering and propelling has been satisfactorily mastered. Had it been otherwise, how is it that so magnificent an achievement has not been forthwith applied to the more noble and remunerative arts of peace and commerce, instead of being shelved for the horrors of war? The moment air ships can be directed, the probability is they will be seized upon immediately to bring about results far more creditable than the annihilation of our fellow creatures.

Secondly. A bombardment from above might, and possibly would, involve a contest in the air. If these agents are available for attack they may be constructed for defensive objects, for retaliation, and for reprisals. One may swoop down like a hawk, but another may rise up like a rocket and bring down its adversary like the stick. And how about the latest arms of precision, chain-shot, and shrapnel? A gas-inflated observatory can often be kept well in the rear in a more secure captive state, but if these flying torpedoes are going in for close quarters, as they must to "spot" their victims, the hazards will be so great that pressed men, rather than volunteers, will have to be forced into the empyrean; and, so far as my experience goes among officers, soldiers, and civilians, I never yet noticed any exuberant bellicose tendency, or display of pugnacity, while exploring in mid-air.

I once took up a gentleman who was said to be very daring, and among his accomplishments was a proficiency with the gloves; a friend of his who was with us thought fit in a moment of pardonable elation to indulge in playful sparring with the reputed amateur boxer. I was rather surprised to notice that he evinced an apparent distaste, and even incompetency, for this sort of thing when aloft. It certainly might have been that the narrow confines of a wicker basket were not sufficiently capacious for manoeuvring, or that a passing nervousness took all the fight out of him. He protested against his friend's familiarity, while casting an appealing glance at me. "Recollect,'. he cried, " where we are;" but on reaching *terra firma* I observed that his facial expression was decidedly more combative, and that he was quite ready then for a friendly exchange of taps; this, with other incidents I could mention, has led me to conclude that the upper air is not altogether suitable or provocative for belligerent performances.

By way of illustration, I may state that Green more than forty years since was engaged to attend with one of his balloons at a park down in Staffordshire, where there was to be an experiment with dropping shells from a battery affixed to the hoop, but no one was to go up, and the aeronaut's services were only required for the preparatory work, as the long range committee preferred to manage matters themselves, so far as the adjustment and discharge of the petards went. They selected a central spot in a wood as the area for their intended demolition, but on setting the balloon free they neglected Green's hint to look out for a veering current, in case they had not provided a remedy, as he had, if his services had been retained for the most critical part of the undertaking. Well, the experimentalists disregarded the expert, but when the missiles were discharged they flew bang at friendly spectators instead of the camping ground of an ideal enemy, thus causing a helter-skelter stampede, including a bevy of policemen—in short, the whole affair was a fiasco; and it might have been so easily prevented, as Green's foresight had led him to think of a compensating plan to cause the balloon to go straight in the desired course; but the enthusiasts did not believe that a past master was

necessary for aeronautic transactions, and it will not be surprising if some of the military adventurers to whom we have been referring find themselves similarly situated.

Last year I read that two intrepid Frenchmen made a trip to our shores from Cherbourg, and threw down as they passed some yachts near the coast a number of cork balls painted white, just, sportively of course, to see how they would act as the lightest and most harmless of grenades, without, as we may charitably conclude, any ulterior designs such as the First Napoleon is credited with when the aerial flotilla at Boulogne was talked about. But, really, in the present day, when the blowing up of ironclads is a recognized feature of warfare, and when torpedo boats can dive and make straightway at a man-of-war to strike below the belt, it is time to be on the *qui vive*, and though aeronauts may feel no great alarm about an unexpected visit from a torpedo fleet, knowing, as they do, that the air is more than eight hundred times lighter than water, and that the difficulties to be first surmounted are proportionately great, still, there is no denying that the route overhead is open to all nations, and that a scare, lest any unwelcome guests should arrive, has actually been felt as to the possibility of their turning up from beneath the Channel. We know that John Bull and all true Britons would rather face an adversary from above, than if he were to crawl and pounce upon us from below.

But at present we need not quake as to the high or subway route.

One of the latest and most interesting phases of this subject relates to Lord Wolseley's maiden ascent from the grounds at Lidsing, near Chatham, and to various active preparations on the Continent which have a character of their own, and are essentially dissimilar to the experiments in Great Britain.

An illustrious man undergoing his initiation in the balloon car, forms an event which is not of every day occurrence, and must prove very encouraging to the intrepid engineer officers, and also to the general public, who like to see the leading authority go now and again to the front for the sake of thoroughly inspecting, and of obtaining some practical acquaintance with any new branch of science which may be on trial.

The General's declaration that " he believed *himself* in novelties," must have produced conflicting opinions in the minds of many more conservative brother officers; but what must have been the effect of the next assertion? Namely, "the more novelties the better."

Lord Wolseley believed in what Napoleon said: "You must change your tactics frequently."

The first impression made by his ascent of 500 feet, elicited the General' approval.

In the course of a conversation with one of his staff, Lord Wolseley stated that "had he been able to employ balloons in the earlier stages of the Sudan campaign, the affair would not have lasted as many months as it did years."

We get therefore a very high testimony as to the value of the balloon for military objects, and as the exploits of our war balloons do not amount, at present, to anything particularly noteworthy, the General's encouraging remarks will have an excellent effect, it may fairly be presumed.

The most recent effort in this line, near Dover, was not successful.

The balloon "Sentinel" was filled and essayed to watch the volunteers, but was forced to retire with the most eccentric capers—owing to the freaks of rude Boreas, which was, after all, merely imparting useful instruction, though not particularly pleasing, probably, to the officer who occupied the seat of honour.

It is, doubtless, a matter to rejoice over, that he was not blown out over the adjacent coast line; had he been driven away down Channel in a small skin balloon under the influence of a north-easterly wind, he might have touched the extreme corner of the French coast, or been sent down betwixt the Channel Islands.

Happily, however, there was no fresh fatility to lament over, and the instructions imparted by the clerk of the weather as to the impracticability of captive ascents during strong winds will not be lost, and may prove of the greatest importance, so that it is well worth while, referring to it as a warning for future caution.

As the writer of this piece holds it to be his province, and his duty as a practical man to review both sides of public opinion respecting his speciality, he considers it right to state, that the representatives of the press, like the representatives of our constituencies in parliament, do not all take one and the same view about military ballooning; neither do superior officers or the rank-and-file, who, in these advanced days are quite capable of drawing their own conclusions.

A paragraph which I read in the Court Society Review, was to this effect.

"I have very little faith in military balloons for the purposes of observation. In the Sudan no atmospheric conditions, and many were tried, were found to be suitable, for even when the air was dead-still, and brilliantly clear, the balloon waggled to such an extent as to make telescopic observation impossible, or, at any rate, practically useless. At the Easter Monday fight, an infinitely more futile attempt was made to employ the balloon in a stiffish breeze, and the result was, of course, as worthless as the experiment was dangerous.

"All the same, for signalling, especially at night, captive balloons might be made of immense use."

Secondly, we have another rather discouraging experience, which ought not to be forgotten or omitted in these pages.

It is in McClellan's own story, about their doings on April 11th, 1862, and is rather amusing than complimentary to the cause I have so long advocated.

"I am just recovering," the writer observes, "from a terrible scare. Early this morning I was awakened by a despatch from Fitz-John's head-quarters, stating that Fitz had made an ascension in the balloon this morning, and that it had broken away and come to the ground some three miles south-west, which would be within the enemy's lines.

"You can imagine how I felt. I at once sent off to the various pickets to find out what they knew, and tried to do something to save him, but the order had no sooner gone, than in walks Fitz, just as cool as usual. He had luckily come down near my own camp, after actually passing over that of the enemy.

"You may rest assured of one thing," was the remark: "you won't catch me in the confounded balloon, nor will I allow any other General in it."

On the reverse side, it should be mentioned that in a telegram received at Washington during the Civil War, it was stated, "that all the information received from *balloons*, deserters, prisoners, &c., agrees in the statement that the mass of the rebel troops were still in the immediate vicinity of Richmond, ready to defend it."

As a pioneer myself in the service of military ballooning, I heartily wish that something more had been carried out in the decidedly important neighbourhood of Suakim.

I was constantly suggesting plans, among others, to take out an apparatus and holder for the generation of coal gas, feeling persuaded that at a short notice, an enterprising private firm would have sent out an equipment with the necessary men and coals, to generate gas on the old quick and cheap plan, in addition to the compressed hydrogen system. There, are, certainly, some advantages in employing the lighter gas, but several counter and

compensating results might be adduced on the other side, one of which is, that in a hot climate, pure hydrogen will escape quicker than the denser production, and, I have no hesitation in saying, that a small skin balloon behaves itself in a breeze with an infinitely less steady action, than a more enlarged surface with greater vertical power imparted to it, which is one out of many of those secrets of success, which men of long experience are well aware of, and I do believe that a certain amount of co-operation between civilian experts, and the military engineers would be attended with good results.

I am not referring particularly to the English school of balloonists, but to foreign corps as well.

It is a regrettable fact that one cannot perceive in the whole list of balloon transactions in warfare, either at home or abroad, any deeds that are at present conspicuously worth chronicling. The splendid exodus of hastily organised balloonists, chiefly sailors, who went out of Paris during the Franco-German War, can scarcely be called military ballooning.

There was no strategy, exceptional skill, or discoveries to mark and dignify their departure or descent; only a most valuable and timely postal and parcels delivery transmission.

This was excellent auxiliary aid, and altogether *sui generis*, but it was not manoeuvring with the enemy or rendering fresh intelligence which could not be gained by ordinary scouts, I mean in a strictly military sense. The winged messengers (pigeons) were certainly helped in their work by having a lift up on their outward journey; but what we should like to hear of, when balloons show up in war time, is that something important has been seen and reported which would have escaped notice but for the argus-eyed aeronauts.

A considerable amount of bewilderment, as we have said, accompanies a novice's first glance of the earth's surface, when villages, fields, towns and fortresses, are seen under a new aspect, with minimised proportions reduced to the model size, and seen from above instead of horizontally.

It requires a trained observer to make heads, tails, and relative proportions out of the new map, and if any altitude has to be attained, very small machines will not do, they may be light and of little capacity, but they are unable to offer a powerful upward tug, which is indispensable for steadying the balloon when telescopic observations have to be made.

The action of diminutive machines of this kind may not inaptly be compared to the jerking, fitful movement, of certain small birds, such as a tomtit, or a titlark, as contrasted with the soaring power of an eagle, or the steadied poise of a hawk.

The balloon, under which Lord Wolseley took a bird's-eye view, is described as "a magnificent spic and span new aerial machine, constructed of the new preparation of *bullock's skin*, and capable of containing 10,000 feet of compressed gas," by which is meant, I presume, 10,000 feet of hydrogen gas that has been compressed and subsequently liberated into the said balloon.

If I were questioned as to the value of this kind of material for the objects intended by the designers, I should, certainly, not speak disparagingly of it, because I think that skin may be very good in its way, but I believe that a certain quality of silk, all things considered, is more reliable, and if it is heavier than skin, it is more readily repaired in case of fracture, and would better resist the shrivelling effects of a hot atmosphere, and of sudden gusts of wind. Silk is also less tempting to the gnawing of insects.

If it is supposed that the use of skin is a new adaptation, I can remove any false impression of that sort by stating that half a century since, I saw and handled a huge balloon composed of similar animal substance, which was called

The use of the balloon as a "bomber" of hostile towns had been debated in Britain ever since the early years of the century, but the first concrete proposals were not laid down until 1850. Then, following the use of aerial bombardment by the Austrians in 1849 , the British were spurred on to experiment and by the 1870's various schemes were in operation. One such plan is detailed in this illustration dated 1878 which shows a naval captain who has attacked a coastal fort manoeuvring a bomb-carrying balloon over the enemy. The button beneath his finger will release a 500 pound "dejectile" full of dynamite on the helpless soldiers below.

The British again made use of the balloon for observation during the Boer War in South Africa. They also utilised a set of moving wooden arms which could semaphore back messages to those below without any delay. These had been designed by Henry Coxwell, the great expert on aerial warfare, and were of such a size that "whether the day is cloudy or the sun's rays strong, they are so clear and unmistakeable that no doubt could exist as to their import."

Egg's folly. The gunmaker had built an enormous fish shaped affair, and it had, fish like, an air bladder to assist it in rising and descending. I was asked to buy the lot which had been laid by for some years, but it was not to my taste; later on, however, after Mr. Barnum had brought over the dwarf, Tom Thumb, to this country, an exhibition was got up at the Surrey Zoological Gardens, and Mr. C. Green was asked to provide a suitable balloon to take up Tom Thumb for a captive ascent.

The air bladder then cropped up, as it would lift fifty or sixty pounds when filled with ordinary gas, and I well remember witnessing the ascent, and shaking hands with the occupant of the little car.

I was informed afterwards by the veteran himself, that Captain Currie, who was a frequent voyager at that time, wished to train and lose weight, so that the skin balloon would take him up, if filled with hydrogen instead of coal gas.

I do not think the trial came off, but I can vouch for it, that the so-called bullock's skin is by no means a novel departure.

We thus learn that history repeats itself, even in an art which is practically little more than a century old.

If we turn from the balloon force at home, and direct a glance towards the continent, as much difference is to be observed in their aerostatic pretensions, as there is between our small and compact army, when compared with the millions of bayonets (and good ones no doubt) that are ready to do battle whenever the dogs of war shall be let loose for slaughter.

In England, preference is shown for exceedingly small bullock's skin balloons.

In France they are cigar or canon shaped, with steering power and propelling machinery attached. I am referring, now, to the war balloons at Meudon.

Germany inclines to medium sized spherical balloons, composed of silk by preference—and I think they are right—to the calico or muslin balloons in store at Chatham or Lidsing.

Russia, if we may believe newspaper accounts, is provided with an air torpedo, besides Montgolfier, and gas balloons. The torpedo air ship can take up eight hundredweight of dynamite, the application of which I have already pictured.

An American novelty consists of an electro dynamic air ship, in the form of a cigar cut lengthways, which presents a flat underside, and a rounded upper; it is constructed of seven independent cells, which are divided longitudinally, making fourteen separate compartments in all.

Among the attractions proposed for the Paris exhibition of 1889, is a captive balloon, having a capacity of 1,800,000 cubic feet, which will take up one hundred passengers.

Then comes the most wonderful invention of all, a balloon which is to surpass in speed the Flying Scotchman. The German Government is stated to have purchased this monster for a million marks, and the constructor is to have a handsome pension for life. I do not believe it!

Now, if these formidable rivals are bent on mischief, and find an opportunity of indulging their destructive propensities, there will be lively and sensational diversions overhead, no less than frightful work beneath, particularly if their torpedos act their part as expected.

Many scientific men, and all the professional aeronauts, with whom I am acquainted, regard this tall talk, not altogether in a literal and serious light, but as a scare and exchange of swagger between those powers who desire to be thought most efficient in modern appliances for warfare. Be that as it may, there can be no doubt that vast sums of money have been expended, and extensive preparations made, in aerostatic material.

There is something about all this boasting and threatening which is calculated to disturb the serenity of susceptible persons, when they read of hundreds of pounds of dynamite and chemical compounds being cast down upon contending armies, and about forts blown up, especially when it is remembered that no shields or ramparts are ever raised, or dreamt of, to resist a vertical onslaught from the regions above. This mode of attack would, to all intents and purposes, prove a novelty, and the question is, whether the lieutenants of our far seeing general, who approves of new tactics, are prepared to resist this kind of thing should a detachment of air torpedoes swarm like wasps or locusts upon our numerically small army, or should they even seek out our tiny war balloons and demolish them with a fell swoop of explosives.

The bare idea of such an ignominious extinction brings us to the vital question of how such intruders could be sent to the right about, or brought low by arms of precision.

Lieutenant B. Baden-Powell, in his able lecture at the Royal United Service Institution, took the danger into consideration; not I think under any apprehension about the descent of dynamite shells, but simply of the customary missiles which are discharged from cannon and small arms. We may infer that air torpedoes and such like were not dreaded.

Mr. Baden-Powell starts from an apt and thrilling commencement when he says—

"First then, the chance of being wrecked by shots from the enemy.

"It must be remembered," he goes on to say, "that the balloon would generally be some way behind the first line, and that the enemy would hardly, especially during the heat of battle, pay much attention to it. It is well to remember that if only hit by a few bullets it would not be much damaged, and could be quickly repaired. Both at Frankfort and at Frankenthal the balloons were penetrated by bullets, and at the latter place by nine, but the balloon remained up three quarters of an hour after. In some experiments made at Tours, a balloon was penetrated by bullets at 1,000 yards, but the escape of gas was very slow, and the balloon remained up some time longer.

"*Secondly*—and now comes a case in point which should not be lightly passed over, it is this—

"In 1880 the Siege Operations' Committee made an experiment at Dungeness with rather more disastrous results for the balloon. An eight-inch howitzer was directed on a captive balloon 2,000 yards off, and 800 feet high. The first shot was unsuccessful, the exact range not being known. The second shell, however, burst just in front of the balloon and tore it open. But even then it took fifteen minutes to descend, so that the aeronauts would have been safe." Later tests have also taken place.

Many persons would think, and as many more might argue with some show of common sense on their side, that the actual safety of a party of balloonists after their machine had been torn open by a shell from an eight-inch howitzer was perilous in the extreme; but the lecturer had no such fears probably, as he went on with unmoved visage, I dare say, to remark that "bullets made of spongy platinum had been suggested as a means of igniting the hydrogen in a balloon by mere contact."

But these stirring and well nigh nerve-testing quotations need not be dwelt upon to any further extent, they suffice to show that the risks, without taking into consideration the doings of those horrid torpedoes, have been fairly weighed.

If the dynamiters put in an appearance, and manage by skilful steering to be in at close quarters, then all I have to say is Heaven help those who may be in their power!

While contemplating this all important phase of aerostatics, I sometimes wonder whether these and other equally important ideas have ever entered into the fertile

brains of those whose province it is to lead and direct the military balloon tactics. There are, I have no hesitation in saying, at this critical period of our national history, uses for balloons even in this country, considering its position and possible surroundings, which I could point out if they would be listened to, and which at no distant period may be found unprovided for when most needed.

I recollect when first I talked over with Major Grover, R.E., who went up with me, my plan for using small and large balloons for destructive purposes, I had such a friendly but scathing glance that I at once interpreted his meaning to the effect that "anything of that sort would not be countenanced at head-quarters."

Well, I have lived to draw attention to the very suggestions which were lightly esteemed a quarter of a century since, but I will not allude to any fresh conceptions at the present time.

(Opposite) "The Saddle Balloon" a novel German idea created by an engineer named George Rodek. The caption to the picture which was first published in 1895 tells the whole story: "An engineer named Rodek has rendered himself famous by his daring ascents in his so-called saddle-balloon. As will be seen in our illustration, a saddle with stirrups takes the place of the ordinary balloon car, on which the aeronaut places himself. Around him are suspended the various instruments necessary for meteorological and other observations. The grappling iron is fixed to the belt at his back, and sand-bags are also securely suspended within his reach. A peculiar feature is a powerful incandescent electric searchlight which is turned on at will by the string which he is seen to hold in his hand."

"The Metal Balloon" which was certainly the strangest machine in aeronautical history was the creation of a German inventor, Herr Willi Schwarz. Despite its outlandish appearance, the balloon did actually fly as this contemporary report, dated November 20, 1897 tells us:

"This huge machine is built of aluminium, is about 130 ft. long by 42 ft. high, and has a weight of some 7500 lb. Motion is obtained by a screw propellor at the lower part of either side, driven by a benzine motor in the car beneath. The ascent was made from the manoeuvring ground at Tempelhofer Felde, near Berlin, and at first good headway was made against a strong wind, but unfortunately (probably owing to the gale), the belting connecting the motor and the shafting slid from one of its pulleys, and the whole affair immediately fell in a slanting direction to Schoneberg, one of the suburbs of Berlin. The engineer sprang out of the car just before the ground was reached, but the car and motor were smashed to atoms, and the body of the balloon itself heavily damaged. During the night the hurricane completed the havoc, and next morning the thin shell lay in a heap of ruins. The cost of the balloon was about £10,000." The Idea of a metal balloon was not new at this time, however, for records indicate that a Frenchman named Mares-Monges constructed a balloon of thin sheets of copper in 1842. Like the invention of Herr Schwarz, however, it also plunged to disaster.

A Drama in the Air

Jules Verne

After Poe's The Balloon Hoax, this next item by Jules Verne (1828-1905) is perhaps the best known, if not most easily available, ballooning story. Written in 1852 some ten years before he achieved immortality with the publication "Five Weeks in a Balloon", it underlines his interest in aeronautics and ballooning history in particular. Jules Verne's use of balloons in several of his other novels have made him widely regarded as probably the art's most distinguished proponent.

In the month of September, 185—, I arrived at Frankfort-on-the-Maine. My passage through the principal German cities had been brilliantly marked by balloon ascents; but as yet no German had accompanied me in my car, and the fine experiments made at Paris by MM. Green, Eugene Godard, and Poitevin had not tempted the grave Teutons to essay aerial voyages.

But scarcely had the news of my approaching ascent spread through Frankfort, than three of the principal citizens begged the favour of being allowed to ascend with me. Two days afterwards we were to start from the Place de la Comédie. I began at once to get my balloon ready. It was of silk, prepared with gutta percha, a substance impermeable by acids or gasses; and its volume, which was three thousand cubic yards, enabled it to ascend to the loftiest heights.

The day of the ascent was that of the great September fair, which attracts so many people to Frankfort. Lighting gas, of a perfect quality and of great lifting power, had been furnished to me in excellent condition, and about eleven o'clock the balloon was filled; but only three-quarters filled,—an indispensable precaution, for, as one rises, the atmosphere diminishes in density, and the fluid enclosed within the balloon, acquiring more elasticity, might burst its sides. My calculations had furnished me with exactly the quantity of gas necessary to carry up my companions and myself.

We were to start at noon. The impatient crowd which pressed around the enclosed space, filling the enclosed square, overflowing into the contiguous streets, and covering the houses from the ground-floor to the slated gables, presented a striking scene. The high winds of the preceding days had subsided. An oppressive heat fell from cloudless sky. Scarcely a breath animated the atmosphere. In such weather, one might descend again upon the very spot whence he had risen.

I carried three hundred pounds of ballast in bags; the car, quite round, four feet in diameter, was comfortably arranged; the hempen cords which supported it stretched symmetrically over the upper hemisphere of the balloon; the compass was in place, the barometer suspended in the circle which united the supporting cords, and the anchor carefully put in order. All was now ready for the ascent.

Among those who pressed around the enclosure, I remarked a young man with a pale face and agitated features. The sight of him impressed me. He was an eager spectator of my ascents, whom I had already met in several German cities. With an uneasy air, he closely watched the curious machine, as it lay motionless a few feet above the ground; and he remained silent among those about him.

Twelve o'clock came. The moment had arrived, but my travelling companions did not appear.

I sent to their houses, and learnt that one had left for Hamburg, another for Vienna, and the third for London. Their courage had failed them at the moment of undertaking one of those excursions which, thanks to the ability of living aeronauts, are free from all danger. As they formed, in some sort, a part of the programme of the day,

the fear had seized them that they might be forced to execute it faithfully, and they had fled far from the scene at the instant when the balloon was being filled. Their courage was evidently the inverse ratio of their speed—in decamping.

The multitude, half deceived, showed not a little ill-humour. I did not hesitate to ascend alone. In order to re-establish the equilibrium between the specific gravity of the balloon and the weight which had thus proved wanting, I replaced my companions by more sacks of sand, and got into the car. The twelve men who held the balloon by twelve cords fastened to the equatorial circle, let them slip a little between their fingers, and the balloon rose several feet higher. There was not a breath of wind, and the atmosphere was so leaden that it seemed to forbid the ascent.

"Is everything ready?" I cried.

The men put themselves in readiness. A last glance told me that I might go.

"Attention!"

There was a movement in the crowd, which seemed to be invading the enclosure.

"Let go!"

The balloon rose slowly, but I experienced a shock which threw me to the bottom of the car.

When I got up, I found myself face to face with an unexpected fellow-voyager,—the pale young man.

"Monsieur, I salute you," said he, with the utmost coolness.

"By what right—"

"Am I here? By the right which the impossibility of your getting rid of me confers."

I was amazed! His calmness put me out of countenance, and I had nothing to reply. I looked at the intruder but he took no notice of my astonishment.

"Does my weight disarrange your equilibrium, monsieur?" he asked. "You will permit me—"

And without waiting for my consent, he relieved the balloon of two bags, which he threw into space.

"Monsieur," said I, taking the only course now possible, "you have come; very well, you will remain; but to me alone belongs the management of the balloon."

"Monsieur," said he, "your urbanity is French all over: it comes from my own country. I morally press the hand you refuse me. Make all precautions, and act as seems best to you. I will wait till you have done—"

"For what?"

"To talk with you."

The barometer had fallen to twenty-six inches. We were nearly six hundred yards above the city; but nothing betrayed the horizontal displacement of the balloon, for the mass of air in which it is enclosed goes forward with it. A sort of confused glow enveloped the objects spread out under us, and unfortunately obscured their outline.

I examined my companion afresh.

He was a man of thirty years, simply clad. The sharpness of his features betrayed an indomitable energy, and he seemed very muscular. Indifferent to the astonishment he created, he remained motionless, trying to distinguish the objects which were vaguely confused below us.

MONSIEUR, I SALUTE YOU

"Miserable mist!" said he, after a few moments.

I did not reply.

"You owe me a grudge?" he went on. "Bah! I could not pay for my journey, and it was necessary to take you by surprise."

"Nobody asks you to descend, monsieur!"

"Eh, do you not know, then, that the same thing happened to the Counts of Laurencin and Dampierre, when they ascended at Lyons, on the 15th of January, 1784? A young merchant, named Fontaine, scaled the gallery, at the risk of capsizing the machine. He accomplished the journey, and nobody died of it!"

"Once on the ground, we will have an explanation," replied I, piqued at the light tone in which he spoke.

"Bah! Do not let us think of our return."

"Do you think, then, that I shall not hasten to descend?"

"Descend!" said he, in surprise. "Descend? Let us begin by first ascending."

And before I could prevent it, two more bags had been thrown over the car, without even having been emptied.

"Monsieur!" cried I, in a rage.

"I know your ability," replied the unknown quietly, "and your fine ascents are famous. But if Experience is the sister of Practice, she is also a cousin of Theory, and I have studied the aerial art long. It has got into my head!" he added sadly, falling into a silent reverie.

The balloon, having risen some distance farther, now became stationary. The unknown consulted the barometer, and said,—

"Here we are, at eight hundred yards. Men are like insects. See! I think we should always contemplate them from this height, to judge correctly of their proportions. The Place de la Comédie is transformed into an immense ant-hill. Observe the crowd which is gathered on the quays; and the mountains also get smaller and smaller. We are over the Cathedral. The Main is only a line, cutting the city in two, and the bridge seems a thread thrown between the two banks of the river."

The atmosphere became somewhat chilly..

"There is nothing I would not do for you, my host," said the unknown. "If you are cold, I will take off my coat and lend it to you."

"Thanks," said I dryly.

"Bah! Necessity makes law. Give me your hand. I am your fellow-countryman; you will learn something in my company, and my conversation will indemnify you for the trouble I have given you."

I sat down, without replying, at the opposite extremity of

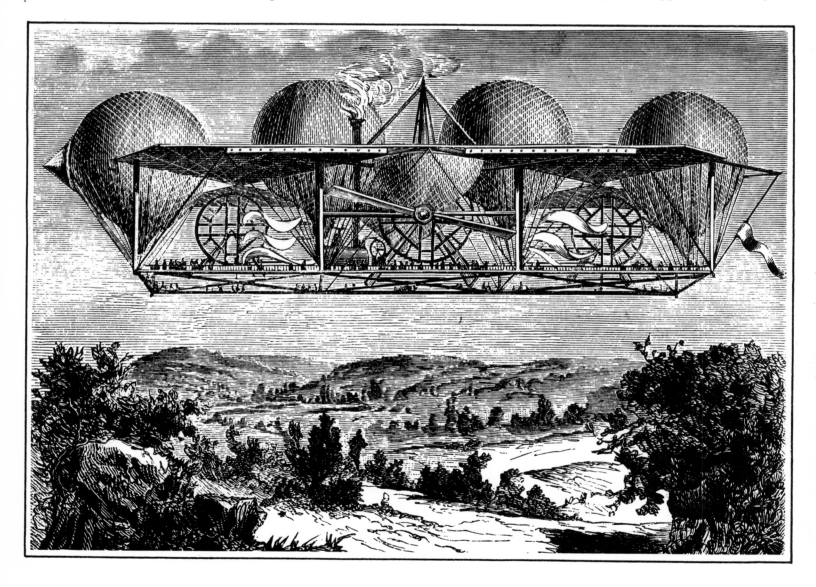

Weird balloon projects were nothing unusual during the latter half of the 19th Century. Perhaps the most adventurous of these was the "Aerial Ship" of the Frenchman, M. Petin which is shown here in a drawing from "L'Illustration" of September 1850. His plan was to link four balloons "each of which should have the diameter of the Corn Exchange of Paris" together with an "immense framework 162½ yards long by about 70½ yards broad". The machine would drive itself forward by the use of a system of airscrews like venetian blinds which could be opened and closed to catch and utilise the wind, "thus the whole machine can be manoeuvred like a ship." If the project had ever been taken seriously it was claimed the "Aerial Ship" could carry "several hundred persons half way around the world."

the car. The young man had taken a voluminous manuscript from his great-coat. It was an essay on ballooning.

"I possess," said he, "the most curious collection of engravings and caricatures extant concerning aerial manias. How people admired and scoffed at the same time at this precious discovery! We are happily no longer in the age in which Montgolfier tried to make artificial clouds with steam, or a gas having electrical properties, produced by the combustion of moist straw and chopped-up wool."

"Do you wish to depreciate the talent of the inventors?" I asked, for I had resolved to enter into the adventure. "Was it not good to have proved by experience the possibility of rising in the air?"

"Ah, monsieur, who denies the glory of the first aerial navigators? It required immense courage to rise by means of those frail envelopes which only contained heated air. But I ask you, has the aerial science made great progress since Blanchard's ascensions, that is, since nearly a century ago? Look here, monsieur."

The unknown took an engraving from his portfolio.

"Here," said he, "is the first aerial voyage undertaken by Pilâtre de Rozier and the Marquis d'Arlandes, four months after the discovery of balloons. Louis XVI refused to consent to the venture, and two men who were condemned to death were the first to attempt the aerial ascent. Pilâtre de Rozier became indignant at this injustice, and, by means of intrigues, obtained permission to make the experiment. The car, which renders the management easy, had not then been invented, and a circular gallery was placed around the lower and contracted part of the Montgolfier balloon. The two aeronauts must then remain motionless at each extremity of this gallery, for the moist straw which filled it forbade them all motion. A chafing-dish with fire was suspended below the orifice of the balloon; when the aeronauts wished to rise, they threw straw upon this brazier, at the risk of setting fire to the balloon, and the air, more heated, gave it fresh ascending power. The two bold travellers rose, on the 21st of November, 1783, from the Muette Gardens, which the dauphin had put at their disposal. The balloon went up majestically, passed over the Isle of Swans, crossed the Seine at the Conference barrier, and, drifting between the dome of the Invalides and the Military School, approached the Church of Saint Sulpice. Then the aeronauts added to the fire, crossed the Boulevard, and descended beyond the Enfer barrier. As it touched the soil, the balloon collapsed, and for a few moments buried Pilâtre de Rozier under its folds."

"Unlucky augury," I said, interested in the story, which affected me nearly.

"An augury of the catastrophe which was later to cost this unfortunate man his life," replied the unknown sadly. "Have you never experienced anything like it?"

"Never."

"Bah! Misfortunes sometimes occur unforeshadowed!" added my companion.

He then remained silent.

Meanwhile we were advancing southward, and Frankfort had already passed from beneath us.

"Perhaps we shall have a storm," said the young man.

"We shall descend before that," I replied.

"Indeed! It is better to ascend. We shall escape it more surely."

And two more bags of sand were hurled into space.

The balloon rose rapidly, and stopped at twelve hundred yards. I became colder; and yet the sun's rays, falling upon the surface, expanded the gas within, and gave it a greater ascending force.

"Fear nothing," said the unknown. "We have still three thousand five hundred fathoms of breathing air. Besides, do not trouble yourself about what I do."

I would have risen, but a vigorous hand held me to my seat.

"Your name?" I asked.

"My name? What matters it to you?"

"I demand your name!"

"My name is Erostratus or Empedocles, whichever you choose!"

This reply was far from reassuring.

The unknown, besides, talked with such strange coolness that I anxiously asked myself whom I had to deal with.

"Monsieur," he continued, "nothing original has been imagined since the physicist Charles. Four months after the discovery of balloons, this able man had invented the valve, which permits the gas to escape when the balloon is too full, or when you wish to descend; the car, which aids the management of the machine; the netting, which holds the envelope of the balloon, and divides the weight over its whole surface; the ballast, which enables you to ascend, and to choose the place of your landing; the india-rubber coating, which renders the tissue impermeable; the barometer, which shows the height attained. Lastly, Charles used hydrogen, which, fourteen times lighter than air, permits you to penetrate to the highest atmospheric regions, and does not expose you to the dangers of a combustion in the air. On the 1st of December, 1783, three hundred thousand spectators were crowded around the Tuileries. Charles rose, and the soldiers presented arms to him. He travelled nine leagues in the air, conducting his balloon with an ability not surpassed by modern aeronauts. The king awarded him a pension of two thousand livres; for then they encouraged new inventions."

The unknown now seemed to be under the influence of considerable agitation.

"Monsieur," he resumed, "I have studied this, and I am convinced that the first aeronauts guided their balloons. Without speaking of Blanchard, whose assertions may be received with doubt, Guyton-Morveaux, by the aid of oars and rudder, made his machine answer to the helm, and take the direction he determined on. More recently, M. Julien, a watchmaker, made some convincing experiments at the Hippodrome, in Paris; for, by a special mechanism, his aerial apparatus, oblong in form, went visibly against the wind. It occurred to M. Petin to place four hydrogen balloons together; and, by means of sails hung horizontally and partly folded, he hopes to be able to disturb the equilibrium, and, thus inclining the apparatus, to convey it in an oblique direction. They speak, also, of forces to overcome the resistance of currents,—for instance, the screw; but the screw, working on a moveable centre, will give no result. I, monsieur, have discovered the only means of guiding balloons; and no academy has come to my aid, no city has filled up subscriptions for me, no government has thought fit to listen to me! It is infamous!"

The unknown gesticulated fiercely, and the car underwent violent oscillations. I had much trouble in calming him.

Meanwhile the balloon had entered a more rapid current, and we advanced south, at fifteen hundred yards above the earth.

"See, there is Darmstadt," said my companion, leaning over the car. "Do you perceive the château? Not very distinctly, eh? What would you have? The heat of the storm makes the outline of objects waver, and you must have a skilled eye to recognize localities."

"Are you certain it is Darmstadt?" I asked.

"I am sure of it. We are now six leagues from Frankfort."

"Then we must descend."

"Descend! You would not go down on the steeples," said the unknown, with a chuckle.

"No, but in the suburbs of the city."

"Well, let us avoid the steeples!"

So speaking, my companion seized some bags of ballast. I hastened to prevent him; but he overthrew me with one hand, and the unballasted balloon ascended to two thousand yards.

"Rest easy," said he, "and do not forget that Brioschi, Biot, Gay-Lussac, Bixio, and Barral ascended to still greater heights to make their scientific experiments."

"Monsieur, we must descend," I resumed, trying to persuade him by gentleness. "The storm is gathering around us. It would be more prudent—"

"Bah! We will mount higher than the storm, and then we shall no longer fear it!" cried my companion. "What is nobler than to overlook the clouds which oppress the earth? Is it not an honour thus to navigate on aerial billows? The greatest men have travelled as we are doing. The Marchioness and Countess de Montalembert, the Countess of Podenas, Mademoiselle la Garde, the Marquis de Montalembert, rose from the Faubourg Saint-Antoine for these unknown regions, and the Duke de Chartres exhibited much skill and presence of mind in his ascent on the 15th of July, 1784. At Lyons, the Counts of Laurencin and Dampierre; at Nantes, M. de Luynes; at Bordeaux D'Arbelet des Granges; in Italy, the Chevalier Andreani; in our own time, the Duke of Brunswick,— have all left the traces of their glory in the air. To equal these great personages, we must penetrate still higher than they into the celestial depths! To approach the infinite is to comprehend it!"

The rarefaction of the air was fast expanding the hydrogen in the balloon, and I saw its lower part, purposely left empty, swell out, so that it was absolutely necessary to open the valve; but my companion did not seem to intend that I should manage the balloon as I wished. I then resolved to pull the valve cord secretly, as he was excitedly talking; for I feared to guess with whom I had to deal. It would have been too horrible! It was nearly a quarter before one. We had been gone forty minutes from Frankfort; heavy clouds were coming against the wind from the south, and seemed about to burst upon us.

"Have you lost all hope of succeeding in your project?" I asked with anxious interest.

"All hope!" exclaimed the unknown in a low voice. "Wounded by slights and caricatures, these asses' kicks have finished me! It is the eternal punishment reserved for innovators! Look at these caricatures of all periods, of which my portfolio is full."

While my companion was fumbling with his papers, I had seized the valve-cord without his perceiving it. I feared, however, that he might hear the hissing noise, like a water-course, which the gas makes in escaping.

"How many jokes were made about the Abbé Miolan! said he. "He was to go up with Janninet and Bredin. During the filling their balloon caught fire, and the ignorant populace tore it in pieces! Then this caricature of 'curious animals' appeared, giving each of them a punning nick-name."

I pulled the valve-cord, and the barometer began to ascend. It was time. Some far-off rumblings were heard in the south.

"Here is another engraving," resumed the unknown, not suspecting what I was doing. "It is an immense balloon carrying a ship, strong castles, houses, and so on. The caricaturists did not suspect that their follies would one day become truths. It is complete, this large vessel. On the left its helm, with the pilot's box; at the prow are pleasure-houses, an immense organ, and a cannon to call the attention of the inhabitants of the earth or the moon; above the poop there are the observatory and the balloon long-boat; in the equatorial circle, the army barrack; on the left, the funnel; then the upper galleries for promenading, sails, pinions; below, the cafés and general storehouse. Observe this pompous announcement: 'Invented for the happiness of the human race, this globe will depart at once for the ports of the Levant, and on its return the programme of its voyages to the two poles and the extreme west will be announced. No one need furnish himself with anything; everything is foreseen, and all will prosper. There will be a uniform price for all places of destination, but it will be the same for the most distant countries of our hemisphere—that is to say, a thousand louis for one of any of the said journeys. And it must be confessed that this sum is very moderate, when the speed, comfort, and arrangements which will be enjoyed on the balloon are considered—arrangements which are not to be found on land, while on the balloon each passenger may consult his own habits and tastes. This is so true that in the same place some will be dancing, others standing; some will be enjoying delicacies; others fasting. Whoever desires the society of wits may satisfy himself; whoever is stupid may find stupid people to keep him company. Thus pleasure will be the soul of the aerial company.' All this provoked laughter; but before long, if I am not cut off, they will see it all realized."

We were visibly descending. He did not perceive it!

"This kind of 'game at balloons,' " he resumed, spreading out before me some of the engravings of his valuable collection, "this game contains the entire history of the aerostatic art. It is used by elevated minds, and is played with dice and counters, with whatever stakes you like to be paid or received according to where the player arrives."

"Why," said I, "you seem to have studied the science of aerostation profoundly."

"Yes, monsieur, yes! From Phaethon, Icarus, Architas, I have searched for, examined, learnt everything. I could render immense services to the world in this art, if God granted me life. But that will not be!"

"Why?"

"Because my name is Empedocles, or Erostratus."

Meanwhile, the balloon was happily approaching the earth; but when one is falling, the danger is as great at a hundred feet as at five thousand.

"Do you recall the battle of Fleurus?" resumed my companion, whose face became more animated. "It was at that battle that Contello, by order of the Government, organized a company of balloonists. At the seige of Manbenge General Jourdan derived so much service from this new method of observation that Contello ascended twice a day with the general himself. The communications between the aeronaut and his agents who held the balloon were made by means of small white, red, and yellow flags. Often the gun and cannon shot were directed upon the balloon when he ascended, but without result. When General Jourdan was preparing to invest Charleroi, Contello went into the vicinity, ascended from the plain of Jumet, and continued his observations for seven or eight hours with General Morlot, and this no doubt aided in giving us the victory of Fleurus. General Jourdan publicly acknowledged the help which the aeronautical observations had afforded him. Well, despite the services rendered on that occasion and during the Belgian campaign, the year which had seen the beginning of the military career of balloons saw also its end. The School of Meudon, founded by the Government, was closed by Bonaparte on his return from Egypt. And now, what can you expect from the new-born infant? as Franklin said. The infant was born alive; it should not be stifled!"

The unknown bowed his head in his hands, and reflected for some moments; then raising his head, he said,—

"Despite my prohibition, monsieur, you have opened the valve."

Price One Shilling Coloured

by Thos Tegg No 111 Cheap Side

Prime Bang up at HACKNEY *or a Peep at the* BALLOON

One of Gilray's brilliant satirical cartoons of August 1810.

"MONSIEUR" CRIED I, IN A RAGE

THE BALLOON BECAME LESS AND LESS INFLATED

I dropped the cord.

"Happily," he resumed, "we have still three hundred pounds of ballast."

"What is your purpose?" said I.

"Have you ever crossed the seas?" he asked.

I turned pale.

"It is unfortunate," he went on, "that we are being driven towards the Adriatic. That is only a stream; but higher up we may find other currents."

And, without taking any notice of me, he threw over several bags of sand; then, in a menacing voice, he said,—

"I let you open the valve because the expansion of the gas threated to burst the balloon; but do not do it again!"

Then he went on as follows:—

"You remember the voyage of Blanchard and Jeffries from Dover to Calais? It was magnificent! On the 7th of January, 1785, there being a north-west wind, their balloon was inflated with gas on the Dover coast. A mistake of equilibrium, just as they were ascending, forced them to throw out their ballast so that they might not go down again, and they only kept thirty pounds. It was too litte; for, as the wind did not freshen, they only advanced very slowly towards the French coast. Besides, the permeability of the tissue served to reduce the inflation little by little, and in an hour and a half the aeronauts perceived that they were descending.

" 'What shall we do?' said Jeffries.

" 'We are only one quarter of the way over,' replied Blanchard, 'and very low down. On rising, we shall perhaps meet more favourable winds.'

" 'Let us throw out the rest of the sand.'

" 'The balloon acquired some ascending force, but it soon began to descend again. Towards the middle of the transit the aeronauts threw over their books and tools. A quarter of an hour after, Blanchard said to Jeffries,—

" 'The barometer?'

" 'It is going up! We are lost, and yet there is the French coast.'

"A loud noise was heard.

" 'Has the balloon burst?' asked Jeffries.

" 'No. The loss of the gas has reduced the inflation of the lower part of the balloon. But we are still descending. We are lost! Out with everything useless!'

" 'There is one more chance,' said he. 'We can cut the cords which hold the car, and cling to the net! Perhaps the balloon will rise. Let us hold ourselves ready. But—the barometer is going down! The wind is freshening! We are saved!'

"The aeronauts perceived Calais. Their joy was delirious. A few moments more, and they had fallen in the forest of Guines. I do not doubt," added the unknown, "that, under similar circumstances, you would have followed Doctor Jeffries' example!"

The clouds rolled in glittering masses beneath us. The balloon threw large shadows on this heap of clouds, and was surrounded as by an aureola. The thunder rumbled below the car. All this was terrifying.

"Let us descend!" I cried.

"Descend, when the sun is up there, waiting for us? Out with more bags!"

And more than fifty pounds of ballast were cast over.

At a height of three thousand five hundred yards we remained stationary.

The unknown talked unceasingly. I was in a state of complete prostration, while he seemed to be in his element.

"Provisions, oars, and rudder were thrown into the sea. The aeronauts were only one hundred yards high.

" 'We are going up again,' said the doctor.

" 'No. It is the spurt caused by the diminution of the weight, and not a ship in sight, not a bark on the horizon! To the sea with our clothing!'

"The unfortunates stripped themselves, but the balloon continued to descend.

" 'Blanchard,' said Jeffries, 'you should have made this voyage alone; you consented to take me; I will sacrifice myself! I am going to throw myself into the water, and the balloon, relieved of my weight, will mount again.'

" 'No, no! It is frightful!'

"The balloon became less and less inflated, and as it doubled up its concavity pressed the gas against the sides, and hastened its downward course.

" 'Adieu, my friend,' said the doctor. 'God preserve you!'

"He was about to throw himself over, when Blanchard held him back.

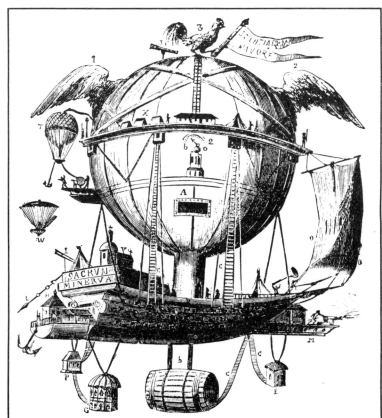

The most famous of all extravagant balloon projects was unquestionably the "Minerva" an "aerial vessel destined for discoveries and proposd to all the Academies of Europe, by Robertson, physicist, 1804."

This incredible machine, pictured here as the inventor envisaged it, was to be 150 feet in length and would carry 60 people in the air for up to six months. The cock and the wings were to be "regarded as ornamental" but the other parts were detailed, seriously, thus:

(a) A small boat, in which passengers might take refuge in case of necessity, in the event of the larger vessel falling on the sea in a disabled state.

(b) A large store for keeping the water, wine, and all the provisions of the expedition.

(c) Ladders of silk, to enable the passengers to go to all parts of the balloon.

(e) Closets. (h) Pilot's room.

(i) An observatory, containing the compasses and other scientific instruments for taking the latitude.

(g) A room fitted up for recreations, walking, and gymnastics.

(m) The kitchen, far removed from the balioon. It is the only place where a fire shall be permitted.

(p) Medicine room. (v) A theatre, music room, &c.

(o) The study. (x) The tents of the air-marines, &c, &c.

"With a good wind, we shall go far," he cried. "In the Antilles there are currents of air which have a speed of a hundred leagues an hour. When Napoleon was crowned, Garnerin sent up a balloon with coloured lamps, at eleven o'clock at night. The wind was blowing north-north-west. The next morning, at daybreak, the inhabitants of Rome greeted its passage over the dome of St. Peter's. We shall go farther and higher!"

I scarcely heard him. Everything whirled around me. An opening appeared in the clouds.

"See that city," said the unknown. "It is Spires!"

I leaned over the car and perceived a small blackish mass. It was Spires. The Rhine, which is so large, seemed an unrolled ribbon. The sky was a deep blue over our heads. The birds had long abandoned us, for in that rarefied air they could not have flown. We were alone in space, and I in presence of this unknown!

"It is useless for you to know whither I am leading you," he said, as he threw the compass among the clouds. "Ah! a fall is a grand thing! You know that but few victims of ballooning are to be reckoned, from Pilâtre de Rozier to Lieutenant Gale, and that the accidents have always been the result of imprudence. Pilâtre de Rozier set out with Romain of Boulogne, on the 13th of June, 1785. To his gas balloon he had affixed a Montgolfier apparatus of hot air, so as to dispense, no doubt, with the necessity of losing gas or throwing out ballast. It was putting a torch under a powder-barrel. When they had ascended four hundred yards, and were taken by opposing winds, they were driven over the open sea. Pilâtre in order to descend, essayed to open the valve, but the valve-cord became entangled in the balloon, and tore it so badly that it became empty in an instant. It fell upon the Montgolfier apparatus, overturned it, and dragged down the unfortunates, who were soon shattered to pieces! It is frightful, is it not?"

I could only reply, "For pity's sake, let us descend!"

The clouds gathered around us on every side, and dreadful detonations, which reverberated in the cavity of the balloon, took place beneath us.

"You provoke me," cried the unknown, "and you shall no longer know whether we are rising or falling!"

The barometer went the way of the compass, accompanied by several more bags of sand. We must have been 5000 yards high. Some icicles had already attached themselves to the sides of the car, and a kind of fine snow seemed to penetrate to my very bones. Meanwhile a frightful tempest was raging under us, but we were above it.

"Do not be afraid," said the unknown. "It is only the imprudent who are lost. Olivari, who perished at Orleans, rose in a paper 'Montgolfier;' his car, suspended below the chafing-dish, and ballasted with combustible materials, caught fire; Olivari fell, and was killed! Mosment rose, at Lille, on a light tray; an oscillation disturbed his equilibrium; Mosment fell, and was killed! Bittorf, at Mannheim, saw his balloon catch fire in the air; and he, too, fell, and was killed! Harris rose in a badly constructed balloon, the valve of which was too large and would not shut; Harris fell, and was killed! Sadler, deprived of ballast by his long sojourn in the air, was dragged over the town of Boston and dashed against the chimneys; Sadler fell, and was killed! Cocking descended with a convex parachute which he pretended to have perfected; Cocking fell, and was killed! Well, I love them, these victims of their own imprudence, and I shall die as they did. Higher! still higher!"

All the phantoms of this necrology passed before my eyes. The rarefaction of the air and the sun's rays added to the expansion of the gas, and the balloon continued to mount. I tried mechanically to open the valve, but the unknown cut the cord several feet above my head. I was lost!

"Did you see Madame Blanchard fall?" said he. "I saw her; yes I! I was at Tivoli on the 6th of July, 1819. Madame Blanchard rose in a small sized balloon, to avoid the expense of filling, and she was forced to entirely inflate it. The gas leaked out below, and left a regular train of hydrogen in its path. She carried with her a sort of pyrotechnic aureola, suspended below her car by a wire, which she was to set off in the air. This she had done many times before. On this day she also carried up a small parachute ballasted by a firework contrivance, that would go off in a shower of silver. She was to start this contrivance after having lighted it with a port-fire made on purpose. She set out; the night was gloomy. At the moment of lighting her fireworks she was so imprudent as to pass the taper under the column of hydrogen which was leaking from the balloon. My eyes were fixed upon her. Suddenly, an unexpected gleam lit up the darkness. I thought she was preparing a surprise. The light flashed out, suddenly disappeared and reappeared, and gave the summit of the balloon the shape of an immense jet of ignited gas. This sinister glow shed itself over the Boulevard and the whole Montmartre quarter. Then I saw the unhappy woman rise, try twice to close the appendage of the balloon, so as to put out the fire, then sit down in her car and try to guide her descent; for she did not fall. The combustion of the gas lasted for several minutes. The balloon, becoming gradually less, continued to descend, but it was not a fall. The wind blew from the north-west and drove it towards Paris. There were then some large gardens just by the house of No. 16, Rue de Provence. Madame Blanchard essayed to fall there without danger; but the balloon and the car struck on the roof of the house with a light shock. 'Save me!' cried the wretched woman. I got into the street at this moment. The car slid along the roof, and encountered an iron cramp. At this concussion, Madame Blanchard was thrown out of her car and precipitated upon the pavement. She was killed!"

These stories froze me with horror. The unknown was standing with bare head, dishevelled hair, haggard eyes!

There was no longer any illusion possible. I at last recognized the horrible truth. I was in the presence of a madman!

He threw out the rest of the ballast, and we must have now reached a height of at least nine thousand yards. Blood spurted from my nose and mouth!

"Who are the nobler than the martyrs of science?" cried the lunatic. "They are canonized by posterity."

But I no longer heard him. He looked about him, and, bending down to my ear, muttered,—

"And have you forgotten Zambecarri's catastrophe? Listen. On the 7th of October, 1804, the clouds seemed to lift a little. On the preceding days, the wind and rain had not ceased; but the announced ascension of Zambecarri could not be postponed. His enemies were already bantering him. It was necessary to ascend, to save the science and himself from becoming a public jest. It was at Boulogne. No one helped him to inflate his balloon.

"He rose at midnight, accompanied by Andreoli and Grossetti. The balloon mounted slowly, for it had been perforated by the rain, and the gas was leaking out. The three intrepid aeronauts could only observe the state of the barometer by aid of a dark lantern. Zambecarri had eaten nothing for twenty-four hours. Grossetti was also fasting.

" 'My friends,' said Zambecarri, 'I am overcome by cold, and exhausted. I am dying.'

"He fell inanimate in the gallery. It was the same with Grossetti. Andreoli alone remained conscious. After long efforts, he succeeded in reviving Zambecarri.

" 'What news? Whither are we going? How is the wind? What time is it?'

" 'What news? Whither are we going? How is the wind? What time is it?'

" 'It is two o'clock.'

ZAMBECARRI FELL AND WAS KILLED

THE MADMAN DISAPPEARED IN SPACE

" " 'Where is the compass?'

" 'Upset!'

" 'Great God! The lantern has gone out!'

" 'It cannot burn in this rarefield air,' said Zambecarri.

"The moon had not risen, and the atmosphere was plunged in murky darkness.

" 'I am cold, Andreoli. What shall I do?'

"They slowly descended through a layer of whitish clouds.

" 'Sh!' said Andreoli. 'Do you hear?'

" 'What?' asked Zambecarri.

" 'A strange noise.'

" 'You are mistaken.'

" 'No.'

"Consider these travellers, in the middle of the night, listening to that unaccountable noise! Are they going to knock against a tower? Are they about to be precipitated on the roofs?

" 'Do you hear? One would say it was the noise of the sea.'

" 'Impossible!'

" 'It is the groaning of the waves!'

" 'It is true.'

" 'Light! light!'

"After five fruitless attempts, Andreoli succeeded in obtaining light. It was three o'clock.

"The voice of violent waves was heard. They were almost touching the surface of the sea!

" 'We are lost!' cried Zambecarri, seizing a large bag of sand.

" 'Help!' cried Andreoli.

"The car touched the water, and the waves came up to their breasts.

" 'Throw out the instruments, clothes, money!'

"The aeronauts completely stripped themselves. The balloon, relieved, rose with frightful rapidity. Zambecarri was taken with vomiting. Grossetti bled profusely. The unfortunate men could not speak, so short was their breathing. They were taken with cold, and they were soon crusted over with ice. The moon looked as red as blood.

"After traversing the high regions for a half-hour, the balloon again fell into the sea. It was four in the morning. They were half submerged in the water, and the balloon dragged them along, as if under sail, for several hours.

"At daybreak they found themselves opposite Pesaro, four miles from the coast. They were about to reach it, when a gale blew them back into the open sea. They were lost! The frightened boats fled at their approach. Happily, a more intelligent boatman accosted them, hoisted them on board, and they landed at Ferrada.

"A frightful journey, was it not? But Zambecarri was a brave and energetic man. Scarcely recovered from his sufferings, he resumed his ascensions. During one of them he struck against a tree; his spirit-lamp was broken on his clothes; he was enveloped in fire, his balloon began to catch the flames, and he came down half consumed.

"At last, on the 21st of September, 1812, he made another ascension at Boulogne. The balloon clung to a tree, and his lamp again set it on fire. Zambecarri fell, and was killed! And in presence of these facts, we would still hesitate! No. The higher we go, the more glorious will be our death!"

The balloon being now entirely relieved of ballast and of all it contained, we were carried to an enormous height. It vibrated in the atmosphere. The least noise resounded in the vaults of heaven. Our globe, the only object which caught my view in immensity, seemed ready to be annihilated, and above us the depths of the starry skies were lost in thick darkness.

I saw my companion rise up before me.

"The hour is come!" he said. "We must die. We are rejected of men. They despise us. Let us crush them!"

"Mercy!" I cried.

"Let us cut these cords! Let this car be abandoned in space. The attractive force will change its direction, and we shall approach the sun!"

Despair galvanized me. I threw myself upon the madman, we struggled together, and a terrible conflict took place. But I was thrown down, and while he held me under his knee, the madman was cutting the cords of the car.

"One!" he cried. "My God!" "Two! Three!"

I made a superhuman effort, rose up, and violently repulsed the madman.

"Four!"

The car fell, but I instinctively clung to the cords and hoisted myself into the meshes of the netting.

The madman disappeared in space!

The balloon was raised to an immeasurable height. A horrible cracking was heard. The gas, too much dilated, had burst the balloon. I shut my eyes—

Some instants after, a damp warmth revived me. I was in the midst of clouds on fire. The balloon turned over with dizzy velocity. Taken by the wind, it made a hundred leagues an hour in a horizontal course, the lightning flashing around it.

Meanwhile my fall was not a very rapid one. When I opened my eyes, I saw the country. I was two miles from the sea, and the tempest was driving me violently towards it, when an abrupt shock forced me to loosen my hold. My hands opened, a cord slipped swiftly between my fingers, and I found myself on the solid earth!

It was the cord of the anchor, which, sweeping along the surface of the ground, was caught in a crevice; and my balloon, unballasted for the last time, careered off to lose itself beyond the sea.

When I came to myself, I was in bed in a peasant's cottage at Harderwick, a village of La Gueldre, fifteen leagues from Amsterdam, on the shores of the Zuyder-Zee.

A miracle had saved my life, but my voyage had been a series of imprudences, committed by a lunatic, and I had not been able to prevent them.

May this terrible narrative, though instructing those who read it, not discourage the explorers of the air.

The death of the English aeronaut, Thomas Harris, who tumbled from his balloon while on a trip with his wife in May 1824.

M. CROCE-SPINELLI

M. GASTON TISSANDER

M. SIVEL

Perhaps the worst disaster in the history of ballooning was that of the "Zenith" which ascended too high on April 15 1875 and led to the death of two of its three passengers. The men who died were M. Croce-Spinelli and M. Sivel while their fortunate companion was the renowned balloonist and bibliophile, M. Gaston Tissander. The pictures here graphically portray the disaster and its fatal conclusion at Ciron.

The Great Balloon Mystery

Robert de la Croix

This report details the strangest story in the annals of balloon voyages—a mystery which still remains to be completely resolved today. Robert de la Croix (1914-   ) is one of the foremost experts on the North Pole and here brings together the facts—both established and suggested—of the ill-fated balloon expedition to the Pole by the Norwegian scientist Dr. Andree and his colleagues.

SPITSBERGEN seldom gets warm summers, but 1930 was an exception. That August two men from a ship carrying a Norwegian scientific mission went ashore on small, barren White Island to look for fresh water. They could see large patches of earth through the melted ice—and then a glint of reflected sunlight caught their attention. It came from the aluminium lid of a cooking pot.

The men looked at each other in astonishment. How in the world could such a thing have got to this uninhabited hump of land, usually ice-covered? They were still speculating on this when they noticed a black object near by. A boat!

Thus began the unravelling of a mystery that had long baffled the world. Ultimately the trail led to the mortal remains of three intrepid aerial pioneers who had vanished 33 years earlier. From records they had kept and undeveloped photographs they had taken, it was possible to reconstruct their tragic adventure in amazing detail.

The story begins in the early 1890's when the dream of reaching the North Pole was a challenge to man's ingenuity, persistence and courage. For three centuries explorers had tried to penetrate the Arctic wastes—by ship, by dogsled, on foot. All had failed; many had not returned.

A delightful engraving of the first balloon ascent within the arctic circle at Tornea Lapmark in the 1850's (opposite), A portrait of Dr. Andree taken shortly before he left for his expedition and (above) an engraving of the leader inspecting the "Eagle" at Spitzbergen on July 2. 1897.

When, in 1894, a 40-year-old Swedish engineer, Salomon August Andree, announced his intention of flying a balloon from Spitsbergen to the Pole, his listeners were incredulous. At the time the longest balloon flight ever made over land and water had been from Paris to Lifjell, Norway—some 800 miles. From Spitsbergen to the North Pole and back would be about 1,500 miles.*

Andree was well aware of the dangers. But he also had tremendous confidence in the balloon and the ingenious system he had developed to guide its course by means of sails and guide ropes. According to his calculations, he could attain an average speed of 17.5 m.p.h., which would carry him to the North Pole from Spitsbergen in about 43 hours. His calm assurance gradually won him much support. The King of Sweden, financiers and scientists, including Alfred Nobel (founder of the Nobel Prizes), provided the backing necessary to construct the balloon; the contract was given to a French firm.

In December 1895, the balloon was exhibited in Paris and attracted crowds of sightseers. By contemporary standards it was large indeed; almost 100 feet high and 65 feet in diameter. The envelope, made of varnished pongee silk in two or three layers, possessed great tensile strength. Most impressive was the gondola, which had a roof and a sort of maintop with a horizontal mast, a foresail and two jibs, having a total surface of 845 square feet.

In the spring the deflated balloon was brought by ship to Danes Island. There the gondola was loaded with supplies and equipment, including three Arctic sledges and a collapsible canvas boat. By August the hydrogen-filled

*The idea of using a balloon for polar exploration was not new. In 1879, Commander Cheyne of the Royal Navy had put forward a similar proposal and committees had been formed in 25 towns to collect subscriptions to finance a British polar expedition by balloon under Commander Cheyne's leadership. Balloons were to be taken to the extreme limit the expedition ship could reach, inflated, and sent off on their voyage. Nothing ever came of the project.

mass of the *Ornen* (Eagle), as the balloon had been christened, was outlined against the sky, above the walls of the hangar that had been erected to protect it from the weather.

The news caused a sensation in Sweden. But some newspapers were frankly sceptical. Where was Fraenkel's body? And why hadn't Horn searched more carefully? In September a party of journalists went to White Island to investigate. Soon the body of Fraenkel was uncovered. The remains of the three aeronauts were placed aboard the Swedish gunboat *Svensksund*, the same ship that in 1897 had carried them to Danes Island for their take-off. All along the Norwegian coast, church bells tolled as she passed. On September 30, 1930, 75,000 people waited in Goteborg harbour as the warship slid towards her moorings.

From Goteborg, escorted by other vessels, she made her funereal way to Stockholm. There the King of Sweden and his nation paid homage to the three brave men who, 33 years before, had set out to conquer the grim Arctic skies.

Now, at last, the world was to know the full story of their tragic adventure, for among the findings on White Island had been a water-logged notebook, its pages stuck together but decipherable. Most important of all, a camera—probably Strindberg's—its exposed films undamaged, turned up. The logbook and the developed photographs told the strangest of all polar tragedies. Bad luck had dogged the flight from the start. Andree, using the few guide ropes still intact, found it difficult to maintain an even course in the shifting winds. Heavy mists obscured the view beneath. Suddenly, on the afternoon of July 12 (the day after they started), the men felt two jolts. The gondola was bumping and scraping on ice. Hurriedly they pitched sacks of ballast overboard. For a moment the *Ornen* rose, then began to lose altitude again. By some

means the weight had to be lightened further. Andree noticed the great buoy which was to be dropped over the Pole as a symbol of their triumph. A moment later the men heard it crash on the ice.

When the balloon rose again, one of the remaining guide ropes caught round a block of ice and held fast. The balloon floated motionless. Andree hesitated. Should he cut the guide rope? To do so would be to surrender all possibility of directing the balloon. They waited throughout a sleepless night. Next morning bright sunshine melted the ice and the *Ornen* broke free. The balloonists celebrated their liberty with a good meal: soup,

chateaubriant, beer, chocolate, biscuits and raspberry juice.

Their joy was short-lived. Three hours later they were scraping the ice again. "We are experiencing shock after shock," wrote Andree. Desperately they tossed out more and more supplies. In the end they realized it was hopeless. On the morning of July 14 they scrambled out of the gondola. A photograph found in Strindberg's camera shows the half-distended balloon lying on the ice like the gigantic body of a dying animal. Their flight had lasted 65 hours and 33 minutes and they were still 500 miles from the Pole.

To reach the nearest land, Franz Josef Land, they faced a 200-mile trip, dragging their sledges over broken ice full of fissures and crevasses. But there were seals, gulls and even bears to be shot. So, as they loaded their sledges, the men were in good spirits. Others had survived a cold winter on drift ice; if necessary, they could too.

For days they marched. At every jagged crevasse they had to fill the gaps with lumps of ice in order to pull the loaded sledges across. "As far as the eye can see," Strindberg wrote in a diary he kept for his fiancee, "there is nothing but ice, great hummocks of it, with channels of water running between."

The great moment when the "Eagle" finally took off to begin its ill-fated journey across the North Pole (Opposite). The photograph (above) was taken moments before the ascent and was the last to be seen of Dr. Andree while he was still alive.

All they needed now was a south wind. But the wind did not come, and with the advent of cold weather the *Ornen* had to be deflated and the take-off postponed. It was not until the middle of the following year that the would-be explorers returned to Spitsbergen. Finally, on July 11, 1897, gusts from the south appeared and they took off.

With Andree were the two companions he had selected: Knut Fraenkel, an aeronautical engineer; and Nils Strindberger, a young, handsome, blue-eyed Viking, who was something of an expert in photography and meteorology.

As the giant balloon rose uncertainly over Danes Island, the basket-like gondola swayed perilously while the men stared aghast at a pile of ropes on the ground. The tugging of the balloon as it rose had stripped away two-thirds of the screw-jointed ropes with which the three aeronauts had reckoned to guide their craft! Nevertheless, the vast sphere sailed off, and gradually grew smaller and smaller until finally it disappeared into the northern sky.

"Don't be disturbed if you hear nothing of us for, say, a year," Andree had said. Even the most optimistic had estimated that, should he reach the polar regions, he would have to winter there. He had taken 32 carrier pigeons to be released at stated intervals, although there was grave doubt

that the birds could survive the Arctic climate. Only one, released a short time after take-off, ever returned. It carried the message, "All well on board. Making good speed."

The winter of 1897—1898 passed with no further word. And when whalers and seal hunters returning to their bases in the spring reported no sign of the *Ornen*, rescue expeditions were organized, one led by the American explorer Peary. None found a trace of Andree and his companions. Then on May 14, 1899, off the northern coast of Iceland, fishermen found a buoy containing a note: "Dropped from Andree's balloon on July 11, 1897, at 10.55 p.m." In September 1899, the main buoy, which Andree was to have dropped over the North Pole, was washed ashore on Kong Karls Land in Spitsbergen with no message.

Years passed. Then, in August 1930, came the eventful discovery of the aluminium lid and the boat on White Island. When the Norwegians examined the canvas boat, they found inside it: kitchen utensils, tins of food, navigation instruments, a canvas bag. On the bag, just decipherable, were the words "Andree's Polar Expedition 1896."

Carefully they removed other objects from the icy slush in

the boat—more tins of food, rifles, an anemometer, an oil stove. Then, under the melting ice and snow, they saw the body of a man, his fleshless kneebones showing through torn trousers. "Look," exclaimed Gunnar Horn, the expedition's leader, "there's an initial inside the jacket. It's an A. We've found Andree's body!"

About 20 yards away they found another body, covered Arctic fashion with a cairn of stones. An S on his clothes told the story. This was the tomb of young Strindberg.

By the end of July their hope of survival was almost shattered. Calculating their position. They found that instead of heading for the west as they had supposed, they had been travelling eastwards, a direction from which they could expect no help whatever. Supplies were growing short; they had had to abandon some food to lighten their load. In their notes the men now began to pay as much attention to food as they did to scientific matters. One day Strindberg wrote: "Coffee—one teaspoonful each, strictly measured, to two and a half pints of water (grounds are not wasted)."

In August they killed a bear, which raised their spirits. Then on September 18 the Arctic silence was broken by their cheers. Land ahead! They were sure they had arrived at White Island. The ice floe they were on seemed to be wedged into the ice offshore. Hoping that the floe would gradually drift southwards towards White Island's shore, they apparently decided to stay on it, and immediately Strindberg turned himself into an ice-mason. Mixing fresh water with snow, he built walls for a compact hut. On September 28 they moved in and felt safe for the first time since their departure.

But fate was already closing in. Early in the morning of October 2, while they were sleeping, a tremendous crackling sound caused them to leap up in alarm. The walls of the hut broke open, the roof split, the floor heaved up and water was everywhere. Desperately they sprang from block to block trying to rescue their scattered stores.

After that, everything is in doubt and speculation. Obviously the three men reached the shore of White Island. The last decipherable words in the record are fragmentary: "Obscurity . . . snow hut . . . transporting out things . . . difficult job." The final moments are shrouded in mystery. Only one thing is certain: young Strindberg must have died first, for his companions gave him a proper resting place. As for Andree and Fraenkel, it is to be hoped that the cold took them gently, in their sleep.

A suggested method of crossing the Arctic wastes by balloon which attracted a good deal of publicity in the closing years of the 19th Century. The idea was proposed by a British naval officer, Commander Cheyne, who believed that working together and utilising trail-ropes, three balloons together would be able to succeed in crossing the pole where one would fail.

A grim souvenir (left) of Andree's last voyage — a copy of the circulars which the balloonists were to drop over Siberia giving the inhabitants instructions as to how to help them land.

A Balloon Journey

Sir Arthur Conan Doyle

Sir Arthur Conan Doyle (1859-1930) creator of the world famous detective Sherlock Holmes, typifies many of the distinguished men of his time who demonstrated a tremendous curiosity in balloons and ballooning. A number of his short stories were influenced by his involvement with lighter-than-air machines and this short report must rank as one of the most singular in balloon literature.

No doubt the coming science of aviation will develop the same qualities as motor driving to an even higher degree. It is a form of sport in which I have only aspirations and little experience.

I had one balloon ascent in which we covered some 25 miles and ascended 6,000 feet, which was so delightful an expedition that I have always been eager for another and a longer one.

A man has a natural trepidation the first time he leaves the ground, but I remember that, as I stood by the basket with the gas-bag swinging about above me and the assistants clinging to the ropes, some one pointed out an elderly gentleman and said: "That is the famous Mr. So-and-So, the aeronaut." I saw a venerable person and I asked how many ascents he had made. "About a thousand," was the answer.

No eloquence or reasoning could have convinced me so completely that I might get into the basket with a cheerful mind, though I will admit that for the first minute or so one feels very strange, and keeps an uncommonly tight grip of the sideropes. This soon passes, however, and one is lost in the wonder of the prospect and the glorious feeling of freedom and detachment.

As in a ship, it is the moment of nearing land once more which is the moment of danger—or, at least, of discomfort; but beyond a bump or two, we came to rest very quietly in the heart of a Kentish hop-field.

I had one aeroplane excursion in rather early days, but the experience was not entirely a pleasant one. Machines were under-engined in those days and very much at the mercy of the wind. We went up at Hendon—May 25, 1911, the date—but the machine was a heavy bi-plane, and though it went down wind like a swallow it was more serious when we turned and found, looking down, that the objects below us were stationary or even inclined to drift backwards.

However, we got back to the field at last, and I think the pilot was as relieved as I. What impressed me most was the terrible racket of the propeller, comparing so unfavourably with the delicious calm of the balloon journey.

One legend has it that the balloon was invented by the Chinese in AD 1300 and flown at the coronation of Empress Fo-Kling. This interpretation was drawn in the late 1890's for a popular Victorian magazine.

An early ballooning photograph (left) of a group of French scientists
about to ascend to conduct a number of experiments. The actual
pilots of the balloon, it will be seen, have been relegated to sitting
among the cords rather than with the men of science! In the second
picture, two English scientists are observing the passage of Halley's
Comet in May 1910. All over Europe similar parties went up by
balloon to study the phenomena and conduct experiments.

Towards the end of the 19th Century the idea of the balloon contest began to develop and grow in favour throughout Europe. The events were in the main held to test endurance, aeronautical skill and sometimes distance records. These pictures are taken from the September 11, 1880 issue of the weekly magazine "The Graphic" and illustrate an event which it had sponsored.

The Gordon Bennett Races (above) were undoubtedly the most popular of all balloon contests and were the brain child of a rich American newspaper proprietor, James Gordon Bennett. He started the event in 1906 and its venue switched from one European capital to another for a period of thirty years. Other pictures here show Nader, the pioneer French aeronautical photographer (top); a proposal for a "Balloon Velocipede" from the "English Mechanic" of 1869 (opposite); and a facsimile of the "Lifeboat Saturday" card dropped from the air on September 5 1903 to raise money for charity.

The Man in the Wicker Basket

John Toland

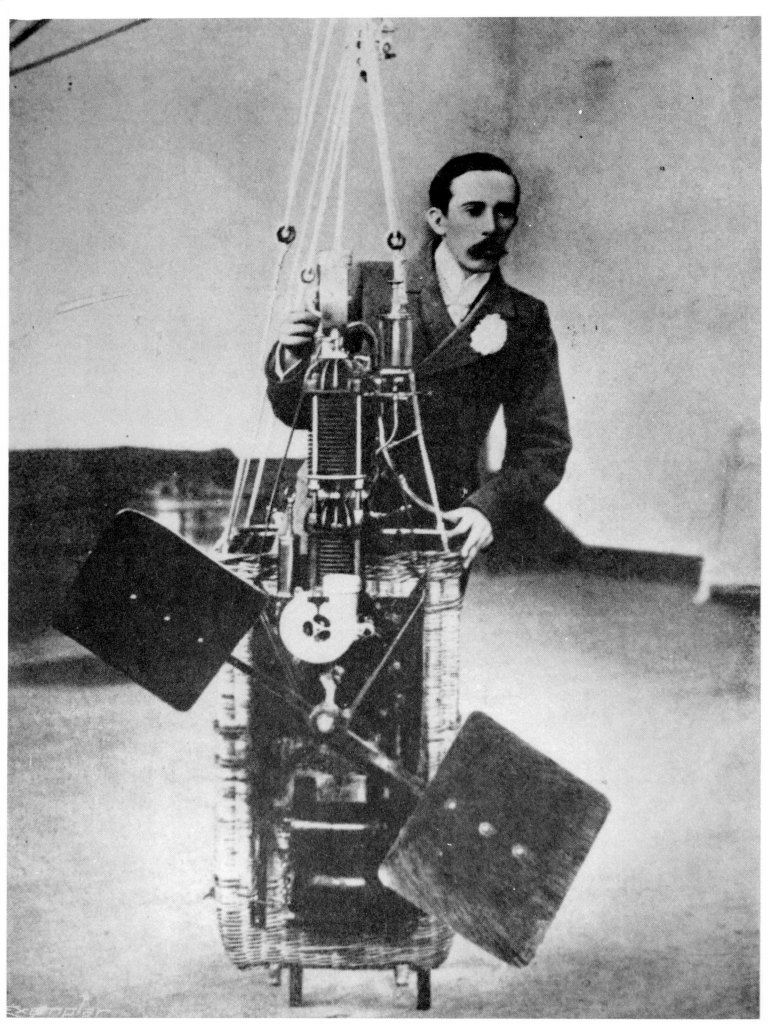

The gap in the story between the balloon and the navigable air-ship is here bridged by Pulitzer Prize-winning author, John Toland (1910-   ) who recounts the experiments in Paris of the legendary aviator Alberto Santos-Dumont. From the achievements of this man, aviation was to take giant strides into the realms of aeroplane flight and—in due time—the space age...

A STRANGE procession was coming across a broad field in the beautiful Jardin d'Acclimation (the New Zoological Garden of Paris) on a September day in 1898. Excited young Parisian dandies, some in caps and gaily checked knickerbockers, others in top hats and frock coats, were guiding their cars at a crawl; and as they drove they kept craning their necks to follow a curious yellow vehicle floating in the air. It looked like a badly-shaped cigar.

Following the belching cars was a large, not-so-fashionable, but just as excited group of students and office workers, with girl friends in billowing skirts that swept the ground. They were jabbering and pointing at the eighty-two-and-a-half-foot airship, which several men were drawing on a long rope toward the leeward side of the field.

The crowd's excitement was understandable. There was a chance—only a slight one, but still a chance—that today, September 20, would be the day man would first navigate the air. It was a moment that would compete with the historic launching of Fulton's *Claremont* or the firing of Stephenson's first crude locomotive. That is, if the clumsy-looking airship actually flew.

A dapper young man about the size of a jockey stood nonchantly in a deep wicker basket suspended by ropes from the gas bag. He was the inventor and navigator of the airship, the wealthy young Brazilian, Alberto Santos-Dumont. He was immaculate in a pin-striped suit, high collar, derby, and kid gloves.

When the floating dirigible approached the tall trees bordering the side of the field, Santos called out an order in a high-pitched, almost effeminate voice. The men on the ropes obediently stopped and pulled the airship down until the basket touched the turf. The Brazilian leaped nimbly to the ground. His peg-topped trousers were worn a fashionable two inches above his ankles, and the heels on his glossy shoes were more than an inch high.

He wrapped a strap around the wheel of the two-cylinder petrol motor that was fixed behind the basket. Then he pulled sharply. The motor started with a series of crashing explosions, and the gathering crowd jumped back in fear. At once several members of the exclusive Aero Club pushed forward and tried again to persuade their colleague to postpone his trip until a safe electric motor could be installed.

One young man anxiously pointed with his cane to the flame shooting several feet behind the exhaust. "It's going to explode the hydrogen in the balloon!" he shouted above the coughing of the tiny engine.

Santos amiably shook his head. It was his theory, and his alone, that the recently invented petrol motor was the only answer to the seemingly impossible task of conquering the air. Solomon Andrews' motorless *Aereon* had proved to be too limited in cruising range. And neither Giffard's steam-driven dirigible nor Renard's electric ship had been able to go fast enough to manoeuvre successfully in the air.

An explosion was the least of Santos' worries, for the flames licking out of the exhaust were a good thirty feet below the hydrogen-filled bag. He felt that the extra horse-power was well worth the risk.

A half-dozen professional balloonists now strolled up to Santos and advised him, in a patronising way, to start from the other end of the field where he could rise and float with the wind. When he refused to take their advice, they shrugged their shoulders and backed away to a safe distance, waiting for the crash they knew was sure to come.

Santos took a final look at the brilliant blue afternoon sky. Then, satisfied, he climbed into the willow car. The guide rope was slackened, and the elongated balloon began to leave the ground.

Now that the final moment had come, the crowd fell into a frightened silence. Everyone recalled vividly his favourite airship accident: Wolfert had been burned to death in the wreckage of his benzene-powered dirigible; just recently Schwartz's rigid monster had blown itself to bits in St. Petersburg; and there were many more—enough, indeed, to dampen the ardour of anyone but an airshipman.

Santos stroked his small but quite bushy moustache and calmly gave the signal to release the rope. To the crowd he looked bored. The ship rose rapidly, and Santos headed obliquely into the wind. There was a shocked gasp from the balloonists, who were positive that the ship would be tossed into the nearby trees. Miraculously, the dirigible did just what Santos had predicted: it bucked the wind. The wind acted as a lever, and in a few seconds the *Santos-Dumont* Number 1 was safely above the trees,

The crowd shouted with relief, then almost instantly became quiet again. The ship had wheeled as if blown around and was now skimming along with the wind. A dozen airships had done as much. The big test was to make steady headway in the teeth of the wind. It appeared that the *Santos-Dumont* Number 1 was going to flounder like all the others.

As if in answer to the doubters below, the big yellow dirigible made a sharp turn over the Jardin d'Acclimation and headed straight into the wind, moving briskly and easily.

The crowd cheered wildly. Women fluttered handkerchiefs, mechanics threw grimy caps into the air, and the young dandies from the Aero and Automobile clubs jumped up and down and waved their derbies and high hats. For the first time in history a powered airship had obeyed her rudder!

The ship was now twisting and turning with utter grace. It sailed in every direction of the compass. Then abruptly it made a steep dive. Women screamed in terror. But then the ship swooped up into a climb. The dive had been no accident—just a bit of cavorting by the spirited Santos.

High in the sky, in the willow car that looked like a laundry basket, Santos was tasting a new delight. Many hours of ballooning had prepared him for the sensation of height, even for the sensation of movement; but he had never before felt the wind blow in his face. A balloon always rode *with* the wind.

His flaming red necktie flapping behind him, Santos exultantly executed a near figure-eight. Then he put two ballast bags in front of him, and the ship dipped. He shifted the bags behind him and the ship rose. He was intoxicated with the power of controlled flight. He was travelling in a new dimension. He was a bird.

Overwhelmed by the splendour of it all, he flew over Paris proper. But when he looked down and saw the lofty rooftops bristling with spikelike chimney pots, it instantly occurred to him that he was frightened. Quickly he headed for the Bois de Boulogne. In a few minutes the fields were an ocean of greenery below, and he felt safe once more. He climbed to what seemed a dizzy height, 1300 feet, then made a circle and started a steep glide toward the earth.

Something popped over his head. He looked up and saw to his horror that the cigar-shaped balloon had doubled up like a jack-knife. The hydrogen in the bag had contracted as the ship fell; the air pump, which was supposed to compensate for the contracting gas, evidently wasn't working; and the bag became limp.

The ship lunged helplessly toward the field of Bagatelle. Santos didn't know what to do. If he threw out the ballast he would rise, and the hydrogen would again expand and straighten out the bag; but when he descended again the

balloon would again collapse. He decided he might as well get it over with.

He let the ship plummet down. Now, as he abandoned hope of coming out of the crash alive, his fears evaporated. Instead he was thinking that in a few minutes he would be seeing his father, who had died several years before.

Three hundred feet from the ground he saw he was falling near a gang of boys. As his 200-feet-long guide rope struck the ground he called in his high-pitched voice, "Take the rope! Run into the wind!"

The boys were bright. They grabbed the trailing rope and ran into the wind. Just as the basket was about to crash, the falling balloon soared up like a kite. Santos landed a few seconds later with only a slight bump. He was ruffled but completely unharmed. Presence of mind had saved his life for the first time. It wasn't to be the last.

Even before the first flight of the *Santos-Dumont* Number 1, the Brazilian with the long patent-leather hair captured the imagination of many Parisians with his daring stunts.

When he was eighteen, his father, the richest planter in Brazil, had given him his emancipation papers, a fat cheque book, and some unusual paternal advice: "Go to Paris, the most dangerous of cities for a young fellow. Let us see if you can make a man of yourself."

Santos sailed immediately for France and, to the wonder of his friends, took up divertissements less traditional than wine and women. He bought one of the new-fangled motor-cars, climbed Mont Blanc, and became an ardent balloonist.

He added a new fillip to ballooning. On his first trip in the air he took along a luncheon of roast beef, chicken, ice-cream, cakes, champagne, hot coffee, and chartreuse. That night he delighted Parisians with his descriptions of his meal in the sky. "No dining-room is so marvellous in its decoration," he told the titled and sophisticated members of the Jockey Club.

Santos was so enthralled by this first aerial trip that he designed his own balloon. Soon his balloon—so small that he carried it around in a valise—was a familiar sight over Paris. But even this dangerous sport became too tame for the high-spirited young man. His interest turned to dirigibles, although everyone told him it was impossible to make one that would actually fly. And when his friends of the Aero Club found out that he was going to power his airship with the petrol motor of his tricycle, they told him flatly that the vibration would shake the airship to pieces.

But Santos was a devotee of Jules Verne and H. G. Wells, and a believer in the impossible. One day as dawn was breaking, he and a friend drove in his tricycle to a secluded part of the Bois de Boulogne. They picked out two trees with low-lying limbs and suspended the motor-bike by three ropes.

Santos' friend then boosted him into the saddle of the tricycle. If the mechanics were right, the motor-bike—like a bucking bronco—would soon throw Santos to the ground.

The young Brazilian took a deep breath and started the motor. To his delight there was less vibration than on the ground. It was his first triumph in the air! What was more, it taught him to trust his own instinct. Against all prophecies of doom he built his first *Santos-Dumont* and made his historic first flight.

Inspired by this success, the young inventor spent the next few years building and testing three more ships, each an improvement on its predecessor. By this time he had become the rage, not only of the young bloods (who imitated his clothes, his moustache, and his speech) but of all the citizens of Paris. He was a strangely contradictory figure. Although he was a man of the world, he was simple and direct, with the tenacity of a peasant. He was the companion of dukes and princes, chauffeurs and air-minded bank clerks. He would often work all morning in his shirt sleeves with his mechanics, and then turn up at the Cascade, the most fashionable cafe in the Bois de Boulogne, for lunch with Prince Roland Bonaparte, the Marquis de Dion, or King Leopold.

It was about this time that Henry Deutsch, a balding, bearded, and highly enthusiastic member of the Aero Club, offered a prize of one hundred thousand francs to the first man who could fly from the grounds at St.-Cloud to the Eiffel Tower and back—a distance of about seven miles—in thirty minutes.

When Deutsch first announced his prize, he was criticised for having set a goal that couldn't be attained. Santos said little, but he became obsessed with the desire to win the Deutsch Prize, and quietly began building the *Santos-Dumos* Number 5, which featured several startling innovations. He built a triangular wooden keel with his own hands. It was fifty-nine and a half feet long and weighed only ninety pounds. The joints were made of aluminium and reinforced with piano wire instead of rope. To the horror of his mechanics he also changed all the suspension ropes to wire, cutting the dirigible's air resistance by almost half.

The four-cylinder, twelve-horsepower motor was allocated in the middle of the keel. Santos' basket was far front. A guide rope hung suspended still farther aft. To it Santos fastened the end of a lighter cord. Now, instead of having to shift sandbags to make the ship climb, he merely had to pull on the string, which in turn pulled back the heavy guide rope, shifting the centre of gravity.

In the summer of 1901 the new ship was finished. Santos made a secret trial at four-thirty on the morning of July 12. Although his rudder cord broke and he had to land in the middle of Trocadero Gardens, he was so pleased with the ship's speed and control that he at last had the courage to try for the Deutsch Prize.

He telephoned all the official judges and told them he'd make a run the next morning. The stage was set for the first attempt in history to fly an airship over a closed course within a specific time limit.

That night Santos slept a few fitful hours near his big balloon house. Not long after midnight he got dressed and began to patrol the field like an expectant father, watching the threatening clouds overhead. By 4 a.m. the clouds had broken up somewhat, but there was a gusty wind from the west.

His friends advised him to postpone the flight; but since he had notified the judges the day before, as the rules specified, he felt obliged to go through with it. At five o'clock the spectators began arriving, and Santos gave orders to fill the gas bag.

At six-twenty the great sliding doors of the hangar opened and the airship was pulled on to the field, its pointed nose foremost. Santos was sitting in the basket in his shirt sleeves, a straw hat tilted jauntily on his head. This morning, contrary to his usual reticence, Santos was chattering and laughing like a schoolboy. The Scientific Commission, appointed by the Aero Club to judge the event, walked solemnly up to the basket. Led by the chairman, Prince Roland Bonaparte, each member shook Santos' hand and wished him good luck. Count Henri de la Vaux, vice-president of the Aero Club, who was planning soon to cross the Mediterranean in a balloon, said he hoped Santos would win. And Henry Deutsch, donor of the prize, wrung the Brazilian's hand and begged him warmly to take no chances.

Now the wind was blowing about six metres a second. One end of the balloon was waving in a sad and flabby manner: the sudden change from the warm hangar to the coolness of the morning had reduced the volume of gas. Although air was pumped into a ballonet inside the main balloon, the ship was still not quite rigid.

A mechanic told Santos the dirigible should be returned to the hangar for more hydrogen. But the Brazilian didn't want to keep the huge crowd waiting. He hopped to the ground and yanked the strap, starting the motor. It coughed and sputtered uncertainly. The head mechanic told Santos the motor needed overhauling.

But Santos would have none of it, even though he knew that if the motor stopped in the air it couldn't be started again until the ship landed. Yet he was no longer the gay and carefree adventurer: with his sombre face spotted with oil and his striped shirt sleeves rolled up, he looked like a workman at his bench. He climbed into the basket, counted the ballast bags on the floor, checked the two canvas pockets that held loose sand, and saw that the guide rope wasn't fouled. Everything was ready for the flight.

Deutsch and several other friends shook his hand again. The official timer, Count de la Vaux, squinted at his watch. The nervous chatter of the crowd stopped. Santos raised his arm and shouted, "Everybody, let go!"

The guide rope was released and the ship rose.

"Six-forty-one!" called the Count.

To win the prize Santos had to cross the finishing line by 7.11 a.m.

The ship rose slowly, drifting toward Versailles, and Santos threw overboard sack after sack of ballast. Those on the ground could see him pulling the rudder lines tight as the ship floated over the Seine. Now it pivoted gracefully and headed for the Eiffel Tower. The big canvas-covered propeller spun so fast that it was a blur, and the ship quickly picked up speed.

In a minute the putt-putt of the motor could no longer be heard at St.-Cloud. The ship got smaller and smaller until it was only a speck in the mist that hung over Paris. As the speck reached the tower it vanished, but a moment later it could be seen emerging out of the mist. A man with opera glasses said he was sure Santos hadn't gone around the tower. Another said he had. The argument was joined, and waxed heavily. It was still going on when a car bounced on to the field and stopped with a screech. The driver jumped out and ran toward the judges waving a piece of paper. Santos had successfully rounded the tower, almost scraping its sides, at 6.45 a.m.

The news spread rapidly, and soon everyone on the field was certain Santos would win. But as the minutes ticked by, the yellow dirigible seemed to be making little headway. At last it chugged over the Seine, fighting a stiff breeze. Now there were only three minutes left. The crowd shouted in unison, desprately exhorting Santos to hurry. But the motor was popping asthmatically; the ship was barely gaining.

It wasn't until 7.22 a.m., eleven minutes later, that Santos finally flew over the judges. Before a landing could be attempted, the ship was driven back toward the Seine, and across it. Twice Santos turned, but each time, like a swimmer struggling against a tide, he was pushed back. Finally the motor stopped, and the ship was swept over the Bois de Boulogne, completely out of control.

"Something's happened!" cried a woman.

Then the balloon doubled up.

"He's falling!"

The horrified spectators watched as the *Santos-Dumont* Number 5 plunged out of sight. A dozen of Santos' friends leaped into their cars and raced toward the wreck. They expected to find him dead.

Half an hour later their roaring, sputtering cars rolled into the large estate of Baron de Rothschild. They could see the yellow balloon tangled in the top of a huge chestnut tree. To their amazement Santos was standing in his wicker basket, high in the tree. He was nonchantly eating a basket lunch sent up to him by his country-woman, the Princess

Isabel, Comtesse d'Eu, Rothschild's next-door neighbour.

"Are you all right, Alberto?" called a friend.

The little man pushed back his straw hat and said, "I should like to have a glass of beer."

The ship had been but slightly damaged by its fall into Rothschild's park, and three weeks later Santos was ready for a second trial. This time the weather was perfect. The ship rose quickly, headed for the tower with no swerving. Though it was six-thirty in the morning, the streets of Paris were jammed with spectators: the first trip, in spite of the accident, had brought Santos and his "miracle-airship" to the attention of the world.

In nine minutes Santos had turned the tower. Most of the many thousands watching were positive the prize would be won, and won easily.

Only Santos realised he was in trouble. He'd noticed a loss of hydrogen half-way to the tower, but since he was making such good time he decided to take a chance and keep going.

Just after rounding the tower he could see the balloon sagging. As he reached the fortifications of Paris one of the suspension wires that held the keel drooped so low it caught in the whirling propeller. Santos stopped the motor before the ship could chew itself to pieces.

Promptly Santos was hit by a strong, head-on gust of wind. Driven back toward the tower, the dirigible began to fall because of the continuing loss of gas. Santos was about to throw out ballast when he saw he'd be blown right into the Eiffel Tower. He let the ship fall.

From the hangar at St.-Cloud it appeared that the ship was dropping like a rock. Everyone realised even Santos had little chance of living through a fall on to the dreaded roofs of Paris. A moment later the ship disappeared below the jagged skyline. Another moment and there came a loud, hollow roar. The *Santos-Dumont* Number 5 had exploded.

The crowd screamed. Henry Deutsch, whose prize had caused the flight, burst into bitter tears.

Firemen at the Passy station, who had been curiously watching the flight, jumped into their engines as soon as they heard the explosion. Within seconds their horses were galloping toward the Trocadero section. Other alarms were rung, for it was generally feared Santos had set fire to one of the busiest parts of the city.

In a few minutes the steel-helmeted *pompiers* rounded the corner of the Rue Henri Martin. A big crowd was looking up at the top of a six-storey building. The keel of the *Santos-Dumont* was braced at a steep angle against the side of a Trocadero hotel. The bottom of the keel was resting on the roof of a lower building. Fragments of the bursted balloon draped down forlornly.

A fireman asked where the body of Santos had been flung. A shop-girl excitedly pointed 100 feet in the air. There, perched precariously on the edge of a tiny barred window, was the indestructible Brazilian. When the balloon had struck and exploded on the top of the building, the keel had dropped, straddling the two buildings. Santos had jumped nimbly from the fragile keel, which was crumbling under him, to the tiny window. Someone inside the hotel had stuck a long pole through the bars, and Santos was hanging on for his life.

The firemen lowered a line from the top of the building and pulled Santos to safety. Half an hour later, after the motor of the airship had been rescued, he came into the streets. There he was mobbed by hysterical women who clung to him and smothered him with kisses.

Reporters asked how he had escaped almost certain death. The little man held up his right wrist. On a chain was a medal of St. Benedict. It had been given to him by the Comtesse d'Eu after his fall into Rothschild's chestnut tree.

The crowd pressed around him, shouting, "*Vive notre Petit Santos!*" He couldn't escape. Young women snatched at his clothing, trying to get souvenirs. Finally his friends from St.-Cloud managed to push their way through to him. Deutsch embraced Santos. He offered to give him the prize then and there if he'd promise not to undertake another flight.

But Santos shook his head in refusal.

"What are you going to do now, Alberto?" asked another friend.

"Why, begin again, of course," said Santos in surprise. "One has to have patience."

That night he began building the *Santos-Dumont* Number 6.

Before his crash into the chimney pots of Paris, Santos had been one of the city's favourites. Overnight he became the idol of the youth of Europe. His two flights around the Eiffel Tower had made him an international celebrity. That September, news of the rapid progress of the *Santos-Dumont* Number 6 was topped only by the assassination of President McKinley.

By now Santos was recognised as the world's leading airshipmen. Count Zeppelin's highly giant dirigible, four times larger than the *Santos-Dumont* Number 5, had proved to be such a dismal failure that it was dismantled. The New York *Tribune* categorically stated that Zeppelin "has now definitely retired from the field"

Santos was to make a third try on October 19, 1901. But

the weather was so bad at 2 p.m., the announced time of the trial, that only five of the judges had bothered to be on hand. A treacherous south-east wind of six metres was blowing at the Eiffel Tower, and those acquainted with aeronautics thought Santos was insane to take off.

As usual the Brazilian refused to listen to advice. He seemed phlegmatic, almost bored, as he posed for pictures in front of his vermilion electric car. He was dressed in checked knickerbockers, coat, and panama hat; and a big flower was stuck in his button-hole. His brilliant socks were not quite covered by extremely high spats.

The new ship was identical with Number 5 except for a more efficient ballonet which was constantly fed by the water-cooled motor.

At 2.42 p.m. Santos got off to a fast start and headed straight for the tower. The huge crowd at St.-Cloud was agog over the ship's phenomenal speed. Shortly the dirigible became a white spot. Then it tilted and sheered off to the left. After a few seconds the white spot veered sharply to the right.

Only eight minutes had passed. A moment later the cheering became delirious as the ship was cut in two by the outline of the tower.

"He's coming back!" shouted thousands of voices.

The city itself was in a state of uproar. The spiral staircase of the Eiffel Tower was crowded with spectators who called out advice and encouragement as Santos cautiously circled them at a distance of fifty metres. Men put up their derbies on the ends of their canes, and women fluttered

scarves and handkerchiefs. The streets surrounding the Tower were packed with screaming enthusiasts.

Suddenly the motor coughed—the cheering stopped. A little figure could be seen stepping out of the willow basket and walking calmly back to the motor.

Seeing the rudder flop uselessly, a man on the platform of the tower shouted, "He's done for!"
Santos, seemingly oblivious to the danger, adjusted the carburettor and spark. In a few seconds the motor coughed and began picking up. The little Brazilian again crossed the frail keel like a tightrope walker and hoisted himself back into the basket. The crowd below cheered with relief.

Several minutes had been lost, and by the time Santos reached the Bois de Boulogne he was fighting for time. Now the cool air from the trees made the balloon heavier. Simultaneously the capricious motor began spluttering again, and the dirigible slowed down.

Just as the ship passed over the filled stands at the Auteuil race course, Santos pulled back his guide rope and shifted weights to the rear. The ship started to climb slowly.

The race-track devotees had forgotten their horses and were looking up. They applauded the airborne hero. Suddenly the motor picked up speed, shooting the ship up at a dangerous angle. The crowd cried out in alarm.

Santos shifted the guide rope and weights forward, and the ship levelled off. In a minute he had passed over Longchamps and crossed the Seine. He knew time was running out, so instead of landing he flew over the finish line at full speed. It was exactly 3.11.30.

He had covered the course in twenty-nine and a half minutes.
Santos turned the ship and landed.

"Have I won?" he cried.

"Yes!" shouted the crowd.

But even as his head mechanic was shaking his hand, the Comte de Dion came up to Santos. The nobleman's face was solemn. "My friend," he said, "you have lost the prize by forty seconds."

Angrily the crowd argued with the judges, who insisted the race wasn't over until the ship touched ground.

Santos, though bitterly disappointed, shrugged his shoulders. "Anyway," he said, "I do not care personally for the hundred thousand francs."

But the crowd refused to accept the judges' decision. As far as they were concerned Santos had won. They hauled him out of his basket like a conquering hero and carried him on their shoulders to the hangar. Many ladies threw flowers at him; others tossed him fans, necklaces, and bracelets; and one handed him a little white rabbit. A few lucky ones managed to pull him to their level and kiss him.

At that moment Deutsch, who had just driven in from Biarritz, reached the field. He ran up to Santos and embraced him. "For my part," he shouted for the benefit of the reporters, "I consider that you have won the prize." However Deutsch was merely the donor of the prize.

At once Santos wrote an indignant letter resigning from the Aero Club. But that night he tore it up. To his friends at the Jockey Club he remarked with great sadness and patience, "It's more difficult, it seems, to have the prize awarded to me than it was to win it."

The dispute set Paris aflame. The press was vociferous. Angry crowds roamed the streets shouting that their "Petit Santos" had been robbed. The judges discreetly remained indoors.

After a few days of public-protest demonstrations the Scientific Commission gathered to take a final vote on the matter. The Comte de Dion was still bitterly against giving Santos the prize, but Prince Bonaparte insisted that the landing had not been included in Deutsch's original requirements. The vote was taken. The result: twelve to nine—in favour of Santos.

The dapper twenty-eight-year-old Brazilian had won through to new acclaim. His popularity rose even higher when he gave the hundred thousand franc Deutsch Prize to his mechanics and the poor of Paris.

In the next few years Santos and his fleet of airships—he built fourteen in all—became the outstanding ornaments of the Parisian scene. To popularise flying he spent £250,000 performing innumerable stunts and demonstrations. He would delight boulevardiers by dropping down from the sky to have a drink at his favourite bistro on the Champs Elysees. It was not uncommon to see his airship sail down the Rue Washington and hover over his ornate apartments until a butler, standing on the steps, would haul him in for lunch. By this time his many tumbles from the sky had won him the nickname "Santos-Dismount", but it was all in fun and affection.

Everyone was Santos-Dumont-conscious. Drinks and babies were named after him. His picture graced thousands of French postcards. If a hostess could inveigle him for a week-end, her entire season was a success. And the Empress Eugenie came out of her thirty years' retirement to see him and his famous airship in the sheds built for him on the beach of La Condamine by the Prince of Monaco.

To amplify his experiments Santos wrote books and articles predicting that there would soon be luxurious dirigibles ("floating houses" he called them), flights over the North Pole, huge heavier-than-air craft that would carry hundreds of passengers and tons of cargo. He even went as far as to disagree with his favourite author, H. G. Wells, who was predicting that the world of aviation was just around the corner.

"What do you mean, around the corner?" protested Santos. "The age of air is today!"

He proved it by new exploits. He flew over the Bastille Day Review in 1903; and to the astonishment of the marching troops and the President of France, he fired a grand salute of twenty-one blanks.

When a Cuban society girl implored him to let her pilot the *Santos-Dumont* Number 9, he gave her a few lessons and then said, "Head for the polo field. I'll bicycle over to meet you."

A few minutes later the crowd watching the Anglo-American polo match was pleasantly surprised to see an airship heading for the field.

"It's Petit Santos!" they all shouted.

Then they saw that the pilot wore a huge hat tied with a veil. It was the lovely Aida de Acosta, the first and last woman to solo in a dirigible.

When Santos was criticised for letting the young lady fly, he answered simply, "But it is not dangerous. Flying is so simple a school-girl could do it." He fervently believed in the safety of flying. When none of the professional chauffeurs dared to pilot Deutsch's airship, the *Ville de Paris*, Santos threw up his hands in dismay. "To think," he cried, "that they are willing to risk their necks daily on the highways and yet they are afraid to go a few hundred feet into the air!"

One summer day in 1903 he landed his airship among the boys and girls at the Children's Fete at Bagatelle.

"Does any little boy want to go up?" he called, remembering his own youthful desires to fly.

All of the boys, French and American alike, clamoured to be taken for a ride Santos chose the nearest, an American boy named Clarkson Potter.

"Are you not afraid?" asked Santos as the airship rose.

"Afraid?" the boy said disdainfully. "Not a bit!"

The age of air had begun in earnest.

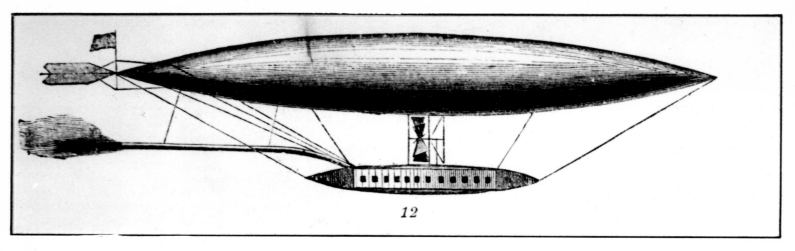

12

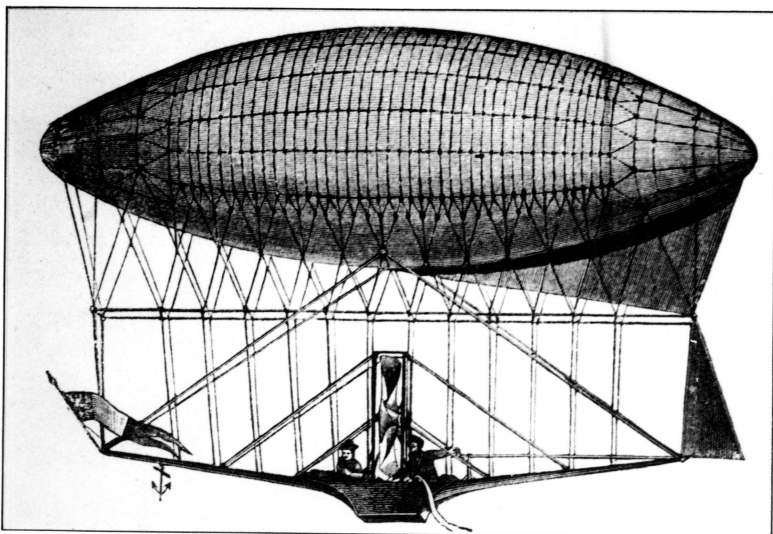

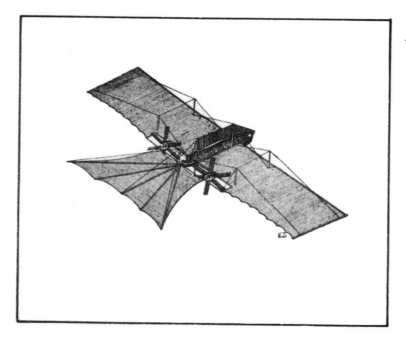

At the dawn of the airship age, each country had its eccentric ideas to offer. America's Rufus Porter proposed a long, thin balloon projectile (top) to be powered by a jet of steam. To match this, the inventive Frenchman, M. Dupuy de Lome offered two variations on the theme of an oval balloon with a propellor driven from the passenger basket to give it speed and direction (above and opposite). An Englishman, William Henson, went perhaps further than both of these, however, with his design (left) for an airship driven by propellors. It was unquestionably a forerunner of the aeroplane as we know it today.

A Day of Cloudless Pleasure

Colette

*In contrast to the hustle and bustle of
the preceding stories, we now return
to the tranquility which is ballooning
at its best. In this story, the famed
French writer* Colette *(1873-1954)
reminds us of the elements that have*
*made ballooning such a satisfying and
continually absorbing activity. Despite
that fact that this article was written
in 1912, its relevance to today's
balloonists is undeniable.*

A bubble which rises into the air, round, well-inflated, golden-coloured, encased within its netting: our balloon. The little car that bears us away seems a tiresome accessory, serving only to delay and deface this beautiful globular balloon whose departure has the slight hesitation and uncontrollable caprice of some bird's wing, but a wing rebellious to the will of man and capable of trifling with him.

It rises quickly and we think it slow. Its imaginary slowness is reassuring, and almost disappointing, for the aeroplane and the motor car have led to an automatic association between a rush of air and the notion of speed. The wind, which previously held the tethered balloon flat against the ground and rocked the trees in the park, the wind now consists of us, the five of us.

Apart from the pilot the car contains the inexperienced but intrepid passenger, the famous lawyer, the seasoned lady traveller, and me. The sides of the car carry, I am assured, enough wine, sandwiches and chocolate to make a landing in a deserted country as pleasant as a garden party.

A bag of ballast empties out into the Seine as we cross it and penetrates the

water with the delightful sound of beads falling. As for us, we are smiling, we are confident, astonished only at moving along without the deafening assistance of an engine, without leaving behind us a trail of smoke, or the smell of petrol, oil or heated iron.

'Six hundred . . . only seven hundred and fifty feet. My friends, please listen a moment! We're leaving the Eiffel Tower on our left, aren't we?'

'Yes, yes, old man, we are . . .'

The pilot is the only spoilsport at this departure. His devoted sagacity restricts our irresponsible delight, and what have we in common with the Eiffel Tower? Instead of remaining satisfied and contemplative like us, why must this pilot fiddle with useless instruments and obstinately pinch the rubber tubing which hangs down from the round belly of the statoscope? We very nearly reward his zeal by commiseration and insults, urging him not to get agitated. Our golden-coloured bubble goes up and up. Why can't he be calm in the same way?

'We're going past the Tower, aren't we?'

'Yes, yes, old man, we are . . .'

This pilot's wonderful! If you listen to what he says you'd think that the Eiffel Tower blocked every route through the air, and that we don't know whether we'll find beside it a little corridor of wind to take us over there, towards that beautiful misty south-east . . .

The pilot, who's more patient than any man has the right to be, makes no reply. Perhaps he's regretting he took dangerous lunatics up with him. And since he busies himself with measuring out careful little spadefuls of the ballast which protects us from the Tower, he lets himself be treated in a friendly way, like a grocer.

'Fifteen hundred . . . two thousand four hundred . . . three thousand feet. My friends, don't be frightened by the jerk. I'm going up to undo the guide-rope.'

Three hundred feet of cable are hanging down from the car at the moment, and beneath the free end of the cable there's still . . . brrr . . . there's still over half a mile of empty space. For a moment the demon of dizziness, swinging on the quivering

end of the guide-rope, beckons to me. But it's a passing weakness and I soon forget it as I recognise the suburbs of Paris, the city's multi-coloured surface, its zinc roofs, its squares and clumps of trees, its bald spots and its blemishes . . . three thousand six hundred feet.

Paris moves away beneath trails of purple smoke, to which the Sacre-Coeur, through a ray of sunshine, brings a harsh, dramatic light. A storm, which is rolled up in a corner of the sky, seems to go down as we go up. The beauty of the sky and the earth, simplified and magnified by our ascent, calms us. Terrestrial sounds no longer reach the cool air where we are hovering, and we remain silent for a long time, until one of us says half aloud, in spite of himself: 'This silence . . .'

Paris is lost, down there, far away already. A glinting patch indicates every bend in the Seine; gardens enclosed by walls reveal to us the secrets of their chateaux protected by forests, the orderly clarity, the unaffected carpet of their French-style gardens . . .

A nostalgic sequence of illustrations from a turn of the century
magazine portraying the delights of ballooning at their most peaceful
and refined, and the experiences to be enjoyed when 'aloft.'

'Four thousand five hundred feet . . .'

The clean, dry air, tasting of snow, brings on the urge to eat and drink; the approaching dusk also revives in us a possibly anxious solidarity and respect—at last!—for the irreproachable pilot. The seasoned lady traveller gives him a glass of sparkling wine, the inexperienced but intrepid passenger offers the assistance of his long arms, while the famous lawyer promises the pilot an invincible plea in his defence, 'just in case, and it could happen, you're involved in some sordid matter . . .'

The pilot smiles gently, like a patient Newfoundland dog tormented by playful puppies. He leaves us to our pleasure, alternately grave and gay; he gives us all he can of the birdless, cloudless sky, the flat world where the distant forests are blue, where towns throw out their suburbs round about

them like divergent beams of a star; he looks at the lozenge-patterned shadow of the rope net immediately beneath the protruding stomach of our golden bubble before saying 'My friends, we shall have to land', before throwing out the opened newspaper which goes down, hovers motionless, then

suddenly twists in frenzy, wheels round like a wounded seagull and falls . . .

Buzzing in our ears, near-enjoyable deafness, we're going down . . . A velvety forest becomes singularly clear, how is it that I can suddenly

make out its russet and green trees, and its round-headed giants? The sound of a waterfall comes up to us, along with a scent just as cool, slightly bitter: the scent of oak trees after rain. What a surge of bird-calls seems to celebrate our return to earth!

'Get down, everyone! Cover your heads and hands!' the pilot's voice calls out.

We've just had time to obey when the car, which had come down on the forest, scrapes the tops of the trees with the crash of broken twigs and torn leaves. Above us the flabby sides of the balloon, which has now gone thin, shudder and struggle. A gust of wind takes us up again and carries us away; I hear a musical twang as we cut through the telegraph wires and I stand up to watch two splendid, plump, mud-coloured huntsmen running below us, hanging from the guide-rope as it drags along, so out of breath and so comical.

We soon out-distance them and I become quite tense as I see rushing towards us two venerable walnut trees, planted at the top of a sloping field. They will not give way like mere telegraph wires.

But the pilot is there! With a rough and masterly hand he saves our lives by pulling the rip-cord: a bump, and the car, like an overturned basket, empties us out on the dry grass of a mown field, all in a heap with the statoscope, the barometer, the last bags of ballast, and alas, the chocolate creams . . .

Little to fear, and no harm done. The centre of interest is the limp-lying balloon, the beautiful bubble that is now burst, killed by each barbarous landing, still quivering as, with each heaving breath, a little more of its dying strength ebbs away.

As it had done in previous wars, the balloon again made its appearance in World Wars I and II. It was perhaps overshadowed by the airship and the barrage balloon, but it did still serve a purpose for reconnaissance and observation. In Germany the Nazis made use of the balloon's crowd-pleasing potential and in the picture (top, left) the "Herman Goering" ascends from the Unter den Linden after a parade in March 1937. An estimated 10,000 people gathered for this spectacle which was attended by both Goering and Adolf Hitler.

These final photographs bring our history of ballooning up to date.

The group of helpers struggling with the balloon (left) were taking part in a celebration to mark the 175th Anniversary of the first crossing of the Channel by Jean-Pierre Blanchard. An Englishman, a German and a Dutchman (Strangely there was no representative of Blanchard's homeland, France) took part in the flight in September 1960 and eventually landed in Belgium, having been driven away from their original destination of Calais by strong winds.

The familiar dome of the Congress building in Washington D.C. reveals the site of the striking picture (above) where Don Piccard, son of the Famous balloonist and underwater explorer, inflates one of his new balloons. Piccard is also shown (left) at Rye, Sussex with his fellow countryman, Ed Yost, before crossing the English Channel in 1963 in a hot air balloon.

The Balloon

Aleister Crowley

Among the many poems written about ballooning there can be few more extraordinary than this example by the occultist and new cult figure, Aleister Crowley (1875-1947). He composed the poem while confined to bed with measles at Tonbridge in Kent, aged 15. In his cumulative volume, "The Works of Aleister Crowley", published shortly before his death, he said "The Balloon" remained "still unsurpassed among my writings."

Floating in the summer air,
What is that for men to see?
Anywhere and everywhere,
Now a bullet, now a tree—
Till we all begin to swear:
What the devil can it be?

See its disproportioned head,
Tiny trunk and limbs lopped bare,
Hydrocephalus the dread
With a surgeon chopping there;
Chopping legs and arms all red
With the sticky lumps of hair.

Like a man in this complaint
Floats this creature in the sky,
Till the gaping rustics faint
And the smirking milkmaids cry,
As the cord and silk and paint,
Wood and iron drifteth by.

Floating in the summer sky
Like a model of the moon:—
How supreme to be so high
In a treacherous balloon,
Like the Kings of Destiny,
All the earth for their spittoon.

Four photographs which capture the totally unique look of a modern balloon contest and illustrate why the events have such a tremendous attraction for enthusiast and layman alike.

Without hard and painstaking work there can be no contest as the picture (opposite) of Richard Jahre, one of Germany's top balloonists, filling his hydrogen balloon clearly shows.

The same applies in the case of the hot air balloon as (above) Terry Adams gets ready to leave in "Jester" from Woburn Abbey during a four-day meeting in 1971.

Once all is ready, the balloons only need the signal to begin ascending — and (opposite) contestants await the gun at the Augsberg Rally in 1965.

Finally, the ladies are always in evidence at these meetings — and here, continuing the tradition of Mesdames Blanchard, Sage and Garnerin, is Christine Turnbull, today's most attractive female aeronaut, preparing to ascend to the waiting skies . . . . . .

Appendix: Balloons in Films

From the earliest flickering days of moving pictures, lighter-than-air balloons have figured large in cinematic history.

The special effects of the pioneer film-makers such as the Lumiere brothers and the King of Phantasmagoria—George Melies—were alive with flying machines of all shapes and sizes at the turn of the century.

Balloons played an integral part in many early films but it was in Alexander Korda's 1938 epic history of aviation, "Conquest of the Air", that they were given the cachet of cinematic respectability. That most distinguished of pilots, Sir Laurence Olivier, played the great pioneer balloonist, Vincent Lunardi.

Nearly twenty years later David Niven was the captain and Cantinflas his crew, as they fled in 'La Coquette' from the dogged Mr. Fix played by the late and much lamented Robert Newton. The film, of course, was the extravaganza by Mike Todd out of Jules Verne—'Round The World In Eighty Days'.

One of the best-known children's films of all time, "Le Ballon Rouge", was made in France by Albert Lamorisse in the mid-fifties. It featured hundreds of coloured balloons and one, a red balloon, in particular. In 1960 Lamorisse made another beautiful escapist children's film, using the same boy as in "Le Ballon Rouge"—this time with a full-size balloon. The film appears occasionally on television and is called "Voyage En Ballon" or "Stowaway In The Sky"

In 1967 Albert Finney directed and starred in the under-rated "Charlie Bubbles". It ended with Finney escaping from all his confusion by drifting away in a balloon.

Two years later, Richard Lester enlisted a superb cast including Peter Cook, Dudley Moore, Arthur Lowe, Spike Milligan and Rita Tushingham to attempt John Antrobus's play "The Bed-Sitting Room". His degree of success is arguable; the particular interest of the film for this book lies in the balloon flown by Peter Cook and Dudley Moore. Its uniqueness lay in its 'basket'—it was a wrecked police 'panda car'!

The most recent balloon film is John Lennon's 1971 short film 'Apotheosis.' This was shot from a balloon as it rises from the ground and enters a belt of fog. At this point, a newspaper report commented: "For nearly fifteen minutes the audience faced a screen that was a complete white blank before the balloon finally broke through the clouds, to the accompaniment of ironical cheers and some walk-outs." (Evening Standard 17/5/71).

The most important balloon film currently being made is the documentary story of a spectacular 2,300 mile pioneer flight across the Sahara. It is being shot by the much respected director, Jack le Vien, who was responsible for the Churchill television film series, "The Valiant Years." In charge of the expedition are two renowned British balloonists, Felix Poole and Don Cameron.

In the last few years there has been a marked increase both in the appearances of balloons in films and, more importantly, in the popularity of ballooning. There is no doubt that the next decade will see an even more spectacular increase in both areas. Keep watching the screens! Keep watching the skies!

Laurence James

Vincent Lunardi's balloon in the Pantheon, London — a scene from "Conquest of the Air" (above).

Sir Laurence Olivier (Lunardi) during the making of "Conquest of the Air" (left).

No more amazing balloon can have appeared on the screen than that used by Peter Cook and Dudley Moore in "The Bed Sitting Room" (opposite).

David Niven and Cantinflas in "Around the World in Eighty Days" (opposite).

"La Cocquette" with David Niven in the basket from "Around the World in Eighty Days" (left).

Albert Finney fades into the sky in "Charlie Bubbles" (right).

The 'star' of Albert Lamorisse's "Voyage en Balloon" (opposite).

The human stars partake of traditional fare in "Voyage en Balloon" (above).

A moment from John Lennon's film "Apotheosis" (right).

Acknowledgements

The editor wishes to extend his sincere gratitude to the
many individuals and organisations whose help and
guidance made this book possible. In particular he would
like to thank the following: Mr. A. W. L. Nayler, Librarian,
The Royal Aeronautical Society; Roger Barrett, Editor,
"Aerostat" Magazine and Vice President of The British
Balloon and Airship Club; Tony Price and Bill Bray of
"The Illustrated London News"; Mary Evans Picture
Library; Keystone Picture Library; London Library; and
the New York Public Library. Messrs. Frederick Muller
Ltd., for "The Great Balloon Mystery" by Robert de la
Croix and "The Man in the Wicker Basket" by John
Toland; the executors of the estate of Sir Arthur Conan
Doyle for "A Balloon Journey" and Peter Owen
(Publishers) Ltd., for "A Day of Cloudless Pleasure" by
Colette. Also Evelyn Glor, Len Deighton, Ken Chapman,
and Lord Montagu of Beaulieu. Finally, my especial thanks
to Tony Lamb, the designer of this book for patience
above and beyond the call of duty and my secretary Mary
Pellow for much the same reason.

The first air holiday makers preparing to ascend in their balloon
from Weilburg in 1836—thus beginning a tradition still observed
today.

SUMMER 77